Ben Early
Aug. 29, 1969

Ol' Man Adam an' His Chillun

Being the Tales They Tell about the Time When the Lord Walked the Earth Like a Natural Man

By ROARK BRADFORD

With Drawings by A. B. WALKER

HARPER & ROW, PUBLISHERS
NEW YORK, EVANSTON, AND LONDON

E-S

"*Well, they was some mighty men in them days and times. And the Lord was beyond them all.*"

Contents

Contents

Ol' Man Adam an' His Chillun

Eve and That Snake

WELL, a long time ago things was diffrunt. Hit wa'n't nothin' on de yearth 'cause hit wa'n't no yearth. And hit wa'n't nothin' nowheres and ev'y day was Sunday. Wid de Lawd r'ared back preachin' all day long ev'y day. 'Ceptin' on Sadday, and den ev'ybody went to de fish fry.

So one day ev'ybody was out to de fish fry, eatin' fish and b'iled custard and carryin' on, to all at once de Lawd swallowed some b'iled custard which didn't suit his tas'e.

[1]

"Dis custard," say de Lawd, "ain't seasoned right. Hit's too thick."

"Hit's got a heap of sugar and aigs and milk and things in hit, Lawd," say Gabriel.

"I know," say de Lawd, "but hit tas'es like hit needs jest a little bit more firmament in hit."

"Us ain't got no more firmament, Lawd," say Gabriel. "Us ain't got a drap in de jug."

"You been usin' a heap of firmament," say de Lawd. "Seem like ev'y time I come to a fish fry I got to create some more firmament. I bet I'm gonter make enough dis time to last a month of Sundays. I'm sick and tired of passin' a miracle ev'y time I wants some firmament."

So de Lawd r'ared back and passed a miracle and say, "Let hit be some firmament. And when I say let hit be some firmament, I mean let hit be a whole heap of firmament. I'm sick and tired of lettin' hit be jest a little bitty dab of firmament when I pass a miracle."

And you jest ought to see de firmament! Hit jest sloshed all over ev'ything so de angels and cherubs couldn't hardly fly, and ev'ybody was standin' round, knee deep, shiverin' and chatterin' and squirmin' round.

"Well," say de mammy angel, "I guess I better

git my cherubs and git on home and dry 'em out. They's shiverin' like they got a buck aguer, right now."

"Don't go bustin' up de fish fry jest 'cause de cherubs is wet," say de Lawd. "I'll dry 'em out."

So de Lawd passed another miracle and say, "Let hit be de sun to dry out deseyar cherubs." And dar was de sun. And de cherubs got dried, but quick as they got dried they got wet again, 'cause hit was so much firmament.

"Dis ain't gittin' us nowheres," say de Lawd. "Gabriel, maybe us men-folks better git out and ditch around some and dreen some of disyar firmament off."

"Good idea," say Gabriel, "only hit ain't no 'count, 'cause hit ain't no place to dreen hit off to."

"Well," say de Lawd, "I guess I got to pass another miracle and make a place to dreen hit off to. Hit look like when I git started passin' miracles hit's always somethin' else." So he r'ared back and passed a miracle and said, "Let hit be de yearth to hold dis firmament." And dar was de yearth.

Well, de firmament runned on de yearth, and

[3]

hit runned in de rivers and creeks and ditches— 'cause firmament wa'n't nothin' but a fancy name for water—and dar was de yearth wid de firmament dreened off and a heap of dry land left.

"Now looky what you done done, Lawd," say Gabriel. "Cou'se hit ain't none of my business, 'cause I got to practice on my hawn all time. But somebody got to go work dat land, 'cause you know good as me dat de land ain't gonter work hitself."

Well, de Lawd looked round to see who he gonter send to work his land, and all de angels was mighty busy. "Well," he say, "I guess I got pass one more miracle to git somebody to work dat land. And I bet de next time I pass a miracle for some firmament I bet I won't git so brash about hit."

So de Lawd got a handful of dirt and made hit in a ball and passed a miracle over hit and say, "Let dis dirt be mankind." And de dirt turn to a man.

De Lawd looked at de man and say, "What's yo' name, man?"

"Adam," say de man.

"Adam—which?" say de Lawd.

"Jest plain Adam," say de man.

"What's yo' family name?" say de Lawd.

"Ain't got no family," say Adam.

"Well," say de Lawd, "I got to change dat. I ain't gonter have none of deseyar single mens workin' on my farm. They runs around wid de women all night and come de next day they's too sleepy to work."

"I don't run around wid no women," say Adam. "I ain't studdin' de women."

"Yeah?" say de Lawd. "But I ain't gonter take no chances. Yo' heart might be all right now, but de first good-lookin' woman come along she gonter change yo' mind. So I'm jest gonter put you to sleep again."

So de Lawd put Adam to sleep and tuck out a rib and turned de rib into a woman name Eve. So when Adam woke up again, dar was Eve, stretched out by his side, wid her haid on his pillow.

"Where'd you come from, gal?" say Adam.

"No mind whar I come from," say Eve, "I's yar, ain't I?"

So Adam and Eve got married and settle down to raise a crop for de Lawd.

So ev'ything went along all right to summer-

[5]

time. Eve was out pickin' blackberries, and de Lawd come wawkin' down de road.

"Good mawnin', Sister Eve," say de Lawd. "Pickin' a few blackberries?"

"A few, Lawd," say Eve. "Adam 'lowed he'd like to has some for preserves next winter."

"Help yo'self," say de Lawd. "Put up all de blackberries you want. And peaches too. And plums, ef'n you and Adam likes 'em. Hit ain't but one thing which I don't want you to tech, and dat's de apple orchard. 'Cause from de news I yars, apples is kind of scarce and they ought to bring a good price next fall. So help yo'self to de berries and de peaches and things, but jest stay out of de apples."

Well, hit jest goes to show you. Eve didn't like apples and Adam didn't too. But no quicker do de Lawd wawk on down de road to Eve see a great big highland moccasin crawlin' long twarg her.

"Look at dat scound'el," say Eve, and she pick up a rock. "I'm gonter mash his old haid quick as I gits a shot at him." So de snake crawls through de apple orchard fence, and Eve climbs over hit.

Well, Eve and dat snake went round and

round. Eve was chunkin' at him and de snake was dodgin' to finally Eve got a clear shot at him and she r'ared back and let de big rock go.

Eve was all right, but she was a woman. And hit ain't never yit been a woman which could throw straight. So Eve missed de snake and hit de apple tree. And down come a big red apple, right in front of her.

"Well, I be doggone!" she say. "Look at dat apple!" So she stood and looked at hit a long time. "I didn't aim to knock hit down," she say, "but hit's down, now, and I can't put hit back. And does I let hit lay, de hawgs is gonter eat hit and hit's too purty for de hawgs to eat." So she tuck a bite.

"Don't taste like much," she say. "I wonder do Adam want to eat hit?" So she tuck de apple out to whar Adam was plowin' de cawn, and give hit to him.

"I don't like apples, gal," say Adam. "Whyn't you give me somethin' I like?"

"Cou'se you don't like apples," say Eve. "You don't never like nothin' I gives you. You got to think of hit yo'self before you likes hit," and Eve blubbers up and commences to cry.

"Aw, don't cry, sugar," say Adam. "I was

[7]

jest funnin' wid you. I likes apples. Give me a bite."

"Nawp," say Eve. "You's jest mean, dat's what you is. You treats me mean 'cause I ain't nothin' but a poor little weak woman and you's a big, stout man. I ain't gonter give you nothin'."

"Aw, honey, don't tawk like dat," say Adam. "Dat ain't de way hit is, a-tall. I was jest playin' wid you. Give me a bite of apple and I buys you a new dress."

Well, when a man go to tawkin' new dresses to a woman he gonter git some action. So Eve dry up her cryin' and Adam et de apple and got her de dress. But dat wa'n't all.

De Lawd seed Eve's new dress and he found out all about hit. And he got mad, 'cause he didn't aim to have nobody on his place which stole his apples. So he bailed old Adam's trover and leveled on his crop and mule, and put Adam and Eve off'n de place. And de next news anybody yared of old Adam, he was down on de levee tryin' to git a job at six bits a day.

Populating the Earth

WELL, Adam and Eve had two chilluns name
Cain and Abel. So when Adam got to gittin'
along in de years so's he couldn't do no heavy
work, he called his boys and say: "Well, you
boys better settle down and git to work. I and
de old lady been s'portin' y'all up to now and
hit's about time y'all was s'portin' me and yo'
maw."

"Well," says Abel, "I b'lieve I'll herd de sheep."

"You smells like a sheep, anyhow," says Cain.

"Boys!" say Eve. "Don't start argyin' and fightin' again."

"Abel started hit," say Cain.

"I bet I'm gonter start you," say Abel.

"And git yo' nappy haid busted wid a rock," say Cain.

So Adam reached for de poker and de boys went on out and went to work. Abel went out and lay back on de hillside, herdin' de sheep and sleepin', and Cain got de mule and plow and started dirtin' de cawn down in de creek bottom.

Well, Cain was plowin' 'long, 'tendin' to his own business, and Abel was layin' back in de shade watchin' him work. To all at once Abel decided he'd have some fone outn Cain, so he say: "Well, Cain, how is you gittin' along wid yo' work?"

"Mindin' my own business; dat's how," say Cain. "And you better mind yo's."

"Me, I'd be skeered to git out in dat hot sun," say Abel. "Hit might cook my brains. Cou'se hit ain't gonter cook yo' brains 'cause you ain't got no brains to git cooked."

"You better go on, now," say Cain. "I ain't botherin' you. But naw, you ain't got sense enough to know when you's happy. So you jest gonter keep on messin' round me to I gits mad and scatter you all over de hillside."

Abel laughed and r'ared back and started to sing:

"What you gonter do when de devil gits you?
Hoe cawn and dig I'sh taters, Lawd, Lawd!"

Well, dat was mo'n Cain could stand, so he up wid a rock and ker-blip! He tuck Abel behind de year, and Abel sort of grinned and rolled over, lookin' jest as natchal as efn he had a lily in his hand.

Well, dem was de days when de Lawd wawked de yearth like a natchal man. So de Lawd wawked up to Cain and say, "Cain, looky what you done did to Abel."

"I ain't studdin' Abel," say Cain. "I was mindin' my own business and he come monkeyin' round wid me. So I up and flang a rock at him and efn hit missed him, all right, and efn hit hit him, all right. One way or de yuther, I ain't studdin' Abel and nobody which looks like him."

"All right," say de Lawd, "but I'm yar to tell

you de sheriff is liable to git you. And when de
new jedge gits done tawkin' to you about hit,
you'll be draggin' a ball and chain de rest of yo'
life."

"Well, what did he want to come monkeyin'
round me for, den?" say Cain. "I was jest plowin' and mindin' my own business and not payin'
him no mind. And yar he come puttin' me in
de dozens. Cou'se I busted him wid a rock. I'd
bust anybody which put me in de dozens. Black
or white."

"Well, I ain't sayin' you's wrong," say de
Lawd, "and I ain't sayin' you's right. Onder-
stand? But what I is sayin' is dis: Was I you,
and scusin' how hard de new jedge is, I'd jest git
my hat and git myself on down de road. And I
wouldn't stop to I got plum out'n de county,
too. And den when I got out'n de county, I'd
take and git married and settle down and raise
me a family and forgit all about Abel. 'Cause
hit ain't nothin' which kin settle a man down
and make him forgit his yuther troubles like gittin' married and havin' a lot of chilluns and
things runnin' round de house."

So Cain tuck de harness off'n de mule and
rid off. He rid for fawty days and fawty nights

and de first think he know he was over in a place name Nod.

"Well," say Cain, "yar's whar I settles down and raises me some chilluns." So he got off'n his mule and tied him to a stump and set down in de shade to wait. And about dat time de Lawd wawked up.

"What you waitin' for, Cain?" say de Lawd.

"I's waitin' for a woman to come down de road," say Cain, "so's I kin git married, like you said, Lawd."

Well, de Lawd laughed and wawked on and left old Cain settin' on de stump tryin' to figger out what de Lawd was laughin' at. To all at once hit come to him.

"Well, I be doggone!" say Cain. "Yar is me waitin' for a woman to git married wid, and hit ain' no woman on de yearth ceptin' Eve, and she done married! Dat ain't gittin' nowheres!" So he sot and figgered and figgered. So about dat time he yared somebody up in de tree singin':

> "I done done all I kin do,
> And I can't git along wid you.
> I'm gonter git me another papa,
> Sho's you bawn!"

So Cain looked up and seed a big gorilla gal

prancin' up and down de limb like a natchal-bawn woman.

"Hey-ho, Good-lookin'!" say Cain. "Which way is hit to town?"

"What you tryin' to do, Country Boy?" say de gorilla gal. "You tryin' to mash me? I be doggone efn hit ain't gittin' so a gal can't hardly git out'n de house to some of dese yar fast mens ain't passin' remarks at her."

"I ain't passin' remarks," say Cain.

"Efn I thought you was one of deseyar mashin' men tryin' to mash me," say de gal, "I'd call de po-lice and they'd show you which away hit is to de First Precinct."

"Looky yar, gal," say Cain. "I ain't got no time to play wid you. I ax you a question and you better answer me right now. 'Cause ef'n you don't I'm gonter bend you cross my knee and burn you up."

So de gorilla gal look like she's mighty skeered. And den she sort of grins and slides down de tree and sets down by Cain.

"I bet you kin handle a gal mean wid dem big old arms of yo'n," she say. "I bet you's a mean scound'el when you gits mad. I sho' would hate to git you mad at me, Big Boy."

"I'm purty stout in my arms," say Cain, "but I ain't so mean."

"You got a bad-lookin' eye," say de gorilla gal. "I bet you's mean to do womenfolks."

"Naw, you got me wrong," say Cain. "I don't b'lieve in whuppin' a gal onless she makes me mad."

"Well, I sho don't want to make you mad, Big Boy," say de gorilla gal. So they sot and tawked awhile and purty soon they up and got married and settled down and raised a family, jest like de Lawd said. And they peopled de yearth.

S*in*

WELL, hit wa'n't long after de yearth got peopled to de people got to gittin' in devilment. And de more people hit got to be de more devilment they got in. And de more devilment they got in, de more chilluns dey'd have. To finally hit was so many people scattered round de place to you couldn't hardly wawk.

And mean? Mankind! They was about the triflin'est bunch of trash you ever run up against. Fust off, de menfolks quit workin' and went to shootin' craps for a livin'. Den de womenfolks quit takin' in washin' and used they kettles to make hard-drinkin' licker in. And de chilluns wouldn't mind they maws 'cause they maws was drunk, and hit wa'n't nothin' to see a boy in knee britches wawkin' round, chewin' tobacco and cussin' jest as mannish as his daddy!

Well, hit come to pass one Sunday mawnin' de Lawd was wawkin' de yearth and he seed a bunch of boys playin' marbles on de side of de road. He look and he seed a boy shoot a marble and knock two marbles out of de ring.

"Venture dubs," say de yuther little boy.

"I said 'dubs' first," say de marble-shooter. So they fit and fit and de marble-shootin' boy was gittin' licked, so he say, "Didn't I say 'dubs' first, Mister?" right at de Lawd.

"You don't know who you' tawkin' to, does you, son?" say de Lawd.

"Nawp," say de marble-shooter.

"You want to say 'nawsuh' when you tawkin' to me, 'cause I's de Lawd. And verily I done

[17]

said unto you, 'Marble not,' and yar you is out yar marblin' on Sunday."

"You ain't my daddy," say de marble-shootin' boy, "and hit ain't none of yo' business what I does on Sunday or any yuther day."

So de Lawd wawked on down de road and he seed a young gal settin' out on a stump, pushin' de 'cordeen and singin' de "Lonesome Blues," jest like hit wa'n't Sunday.

"Gal, whyn't you quit dat singin' dem 'blues' and sing a church song?" say de Lawd. "Don't you know hit's Sunday?"

De gal kept right on singin' to she got done and den she looked at de Lawd and say, "Soap and water, Country Boy." And she went right on singin' again.

"Well, I be doggone," say de Lawd. "I never did see so much sin." So he wawked on down de road to he seed some men kneelin' down in de middle of de road.

"Dat looks better," say de Lawd. "Hit looks like de menfolks is quit they devilment and gone to prayin'. I'm gonter listen and see kin I hyar they prayers."

So he listened and he hyared one of 'em say,

"Big Dick f'om Boston! Come on you six-**Joe**! Wham! Five and five! I shoots hit all!"

Well, de Lawd jest shet his eyes and wawked on. "Im gonter go tell dat crap-shootin' scound-d'el's mammy on him right now," he say. "Shootin' craps on Sunday!" So de Lawd wawked on to where de crap-shootin' boy live at and he knock on de door.

"Who dar?" say a man in de house.

"No mind who yar," say de Lawd. "You jest unlatch dis door."

"You got a search warrant?" say de man. " 'Cause ef'n you ain't you might jest as well go on about yo' business. 'Cause you can't git in dis house onless you got a search warrant."

"Well," say de Lawd, "jest tell Miz Rucker to come to de door whilst I tells her on her good-for-nothin' boy which is shootin' craps on Sunday."

"Miz Rucker ain't yar no more," say de man. "She runned off wid a railroad man, yistiddy."

"Well, send Rucker to de door, den," say de Lawd.

"Can't," say de man. "Rucker's piled up under de table. He been passed out since early dis mawnin'. I's de onliest sober man in de house 'cause I drunk some of dat new wildcat yistiddy, and hit burnt de skin off of my th'oat so I can't drink no more."

"Well," say de Lawd, "dis ain't gittin' me nowheres. Deseyar mankinds which I peopled my yearth wid sho ain't much. I got a good mind to wipe 'em off'n de yearth and people my yearth wid angels."

So de Lawd wawked on down de road, tawkin' to hisself and studdyin' 'bout what he gonter do wid de sin.

"Naw," he say, "angels is all right for singin' and playin' and flyin' round, but they ain't much on workin' de crops and buildin' de levees. I guess I won't monkey round wid de angels on my yearth. They jest won't do."

So he wawked along, studdyin' and a-tawkin'. "Mankind," he say, "is jest right for my yearth, ef'n he wa'n't so dad-blame sinful. But I'm sick and tired of his sin. I'd druther have my yearth peopled wid a bunch of channel catfish den mankind and his sin. I jest can't stand sin."

So about dat time de Lawd comed up on old man Noah, wawkin' long de road in a plug hat and a hammer-tail coat.

"Good mawnin', brother," say Noah. "Us missed you at church dis mawnin'."

"I ain't got no time to go to church," say de Lawd. "I got work ——"

"Yeah," say Noah, "mighty nigh ev'ybody say they ain't got time to go to church dese days and times. Hit seems like de more I preaches de more people ain't got time to come to church. I ain't hardly got enough members to fill up de choir. I has to do de preachin' and de bassin', too."

"Is dat a fack?" say de Lawd.

"Yeah," say Noah. "Ev'ybody is mighty busy gamblin' and good-timin' and sinnin' and goin' on. They ain't got time to come to church. But you jest wait. When old Gabriel blows they hawn they gonter find plenty of time to punch chunks down yonder in hell. They gonter beg to git to come to church, too. But de Lawd ain't gonter pay 'em no mind. They makin' they own fun, now. But when old Gabriel toots, de Lawd gonter be de boss."

"Brother Noah," say de Lawd, "you don't know who I is, does you?"

"Lemme see," say Noah. "Yo' face looks easy. But I jest can't call de name. But I don't keer what yo' name is, you jest come along home wid me. I think de old lady kilt a chicken or so, and den, after us eats and rests up some, you comes wid me to preachin' again tonight."

"I don't keer ef I do," say de Lawd. "Dat chicken sounds mighty good to me. And you say you basses in de singin'?"

"Jest tries hit," say Noah. "I ain't so much on de bass as I is on de leadin'."

"I used to bass purty fair," say de Lawd.

So dey wawked on to Noah's house, and de Lawd didn't let on to Noah dat he wa'n't jest a natchal man like ev'ybody else. So dey r'ared back and et chicken and dumplin's awhile, and all at once de Lawd say, "Brother Noah, I kind of b'lieve hit's gonter rain."

"My cawns is burnin' me, too," say Noah. "Jest slip yo' feet outer yo' shoes and rest yo'self."

"What'd you do, did hit commence to rain, Noah?" say de Lawd.

"Well," say Noah, "I most gen'ally lets hit rain."

"S'posin'," say de Lawd, "hit would haul off and rain fawty days and fawty nights?"

[22]

"I ain't worryin'," say Noah. "In de fust place, hit ain't gonter rain dat long onless de Lawd sends hit. And in de second place, I's on de Lawd's side, and de Lawd gonter look after me do he go to monkeyin' wid de weather."

"You b'lieve de Lawd gonter look after you, does you?" say de Lawd.

"Don't b'lieve nothin' 'bout hit," say Noah. "I knows hit. I does de best I kin for de Lawd, and dat's all de Lawd gonter ax any man to do. I don't do much, but hit's de best I got."

So all at once de Lawd reach inside his shirt front and pull out his crown and set it on his haid. Den he start to tawk, and thunder and lightnin' come outer his mouf. So old Noah jest drap down on his knees.

"Yar I is, Lawd," he say. "Yar I is. I ain't much, but I'm de best I got."

"Noah," say de Lawd, "hit's gonter rain fawty days and fawty nights. And hit's gonter drown ev'ybody on de yearth which is a sinner. And dat means about ev'ybody but you and yo' family. Now you jest git out and build me a ark on dry land big enough to hold a pair of mules and a pair of cows and a pair of elephants and a pair of snakes and a pair of ev'ything which creeps or crawls, swims or flies. And you better make hit big enough to pack away a heap of grub, too, 'cause from what I got in mind, hit ain't gonter be no goin' to de commissary and buyin' grub when I starts rainin'."

"And snakes, too, Lawd?" say Noah.

"Snakes," say de Lawd.

"S'pos'n' a snake up and bit somebody?" say Noah.

"I hadn't thought about dat," say de Lawd. "Maybe you better not take no snakes."

"I ain't skeered of snakes," say Noah, "efn I got a kag of licker handy," say Noah.

"I ain't so much on de licker," say de Lawd. "But hit do come in handy round snakes."

"And wid all dat rain and wet weather, too," say Noah, "my phthisic is liable to plague me, too, onless I got a little hard licker handy."

"Well, you better put a kag of licker on boa'd, too," say de Lawd.

"Better put two kags," say Noah. "Hit'll help balance de boat. You git a kag on one side, and nothin' on de yuther, and de boat liable to turn over. You got to keep a boat balanced, Lawd."

"One kag," say de Lawd. "You kin set hit in de middle of de deck. One kag of licker is enough for anybody for fawty days and fawty nights. I said one kag, and dat's all you carries."

"Yas, Lawd," say Noah, "one kag."

*S*teamboat *Days*

WELL, when de people got so low down to de Lawd couldn't stand 'em, he decided to flood de yearth and drown ev'ybody 'ceptin' old man Noah. So he told Noah to build a ark and ride de flood down.

" 'Cause from what I got in my mind," say de Lawd, "hit look like she's gonter be a mighty wet spring, Noah."

"Gonter bust de levees, is you, Lawd?" say Noah.

"When de levees bustes," say de Lawd, "dat's jest gonter be de startin' of de wet weather. I got my mind set on rain, Noah, and when I gits my mind set, I mean to tell you I makes hit rain."

So Noah got de hammer and de saw and de nails and de lumber and things and went out on de hillside wid his boys to build de ark.

"Dis gonter be a side-wheeler, ain't hit paw? Sort of like de *Stacy Adams?*" say Ham.

"Stern-wheeler, like de *Grace,*" say Noah. "Only bigger. Us wants room, not fancy stuff. —You, Shem! Tote dat planed lumber up on de texas deck. Rough lumber goes on de main deck."

So Noah and Ham and Shem and Japeth hammered and sawed away, out on de hillside, a mile from de river. And purty soon somebody hyars de hammerin' and sa'nters up to ax Noah what he doin'.

"Buildin' you a house, is you, Noah?" say a man.

"Nawp," say Noah. "I's buildin' a ark."

"Well, whyn't you build hit by de river so hit'll float?" say de man.

"Who buildin' dis ark?" say Noah. "Me or you?"

[27]

So de man wawked off and told his wife. "Old Noah is plum crazy," he say. "Buildin' hit right out on de hillside, a mile or more from de river."

"You ain't tellin' me no news," say de man's wife. "Ain't old Miz Noah tellin' ev'ybody hit gonter rain fawty days and fawty nights and folks which ain't on de ark gonter git drownded?"

"De whole family is plum crazy," say de man. "And was I you, old lady, I wouldn't go round wid Miz Noah much. 'Cause de first thing you know you'll be gittin' a hard name, too."

"Humph!" say de wife. "Hit was me which got hit started to resolve her outn de buryin' society."

So dat's de way tawk went round, to first thing you know de young folks yared de news and they went out to see for theyselves.

"Whyn't you make dat texas bigger?" say a young gal. "Efn hit was bigger, us could have a excursion and dance."

"I ain't studdin' excursions," say Noah, "and I ain't studdin' dances. And what's more, y'all young ladies better drag yo'self on down de road, 'cause sometimes I misses my nail and I hits my finger. And when I mashes my finger I most gen'ally cusses some. And hit ain't nice to cuss before young gals."

So de gal laughs and says, "Dat's all right, granddaddy. You jest mash yo' finger and let me cuss for you."

So dat's about de way things run along to old Noah got de ark finished. Den about supper time one night hit started to rainin'. And old Noah reach up and got de whistle rope and blowed a long, two shorts, and a long.

"Git dat engine fired up, Shem," say Noah. "Us gonter be gittin' away from dis man's town purty soon. Git de steam up, son."

So Noah went and stood on de gangplank and marked down de animals which started comin' when they yared de whistle. De mules and de cows and de jay-raffs and de elephants and de lines and de monkeys. Hit was worse den de circus, de way they marched on, two by two, and hit rainin' and thunderin' and goin' on.

"Dis rain look mighty bad for my phthisic," say Noah. "Maybe I better git me a snort of dat red-eye before I gits tuck down sick."

"Git away from dat kag," holler Miz Noah. "Hit ain't no snake bit you yit, 'cause de snakes ain't come on boa'd yit."

"Yeah?" say Noah. "S'posin' I gits tuck down wid de phthisic? Who gonter pilot de boat? We'd be hung up on a sandbar before you kin bat yo' eyes." So he tuck a long pull at de kag.

So about de time Noah got back to de gang-plank, yar come a pair of cotton-mouf moccasins, crawlin' up de plank, slow and stiddy.

"Great day in de mawnin'!" say Noah. "Efn one of dem boys ups and bites me, I'd die before I gits to de licker kag. Maybe now ——" So he sa'nters over to de kag and takes another pull to git ready in case one of dem snakes bites him.

So when he got back to de plank, yar come a pair of diamond back rattlers, hissin' and a-rattlin' and a-strikin' out yar and yonder.

"Easy," say Noah. "Easy, snakes. Jest wait to I git back before you bites me." So he went and tuck another pull at de kag.

And when he got back he seed three copperhaids a-prancin' up de plank, snortin' and singin' and hollerin' for meat.

"I'm jest natchally standin' too far from dat kag," say Noah, and he staggers on back to de kag and sets down. And he seed so many kinds of snakes dat he jest natchally got tired and sleepy and de first thing he knowed he was asleep.

[30]

Well, finally he woke up and he thought he yared de bell ringin'.

"Wait a minute, Shem," he say. "Le's don't pull out and leave all dem snakes in de flood." Den he opened his eyes and seed Miz Noah standin' over him wid a rollin'-pin.

"I knew I could wake you wid a rollin'-pin," she say, and she dragged de rollin'-pin across his haid again. "Come yar yellin' about snakes and hangin' on dat licker kag whilst us was driftin' out in de storm." Wham! "I told you to let dat licker alone."

Well, purty soon Noah got straightened out and tuck charge of de boat whilst Miz Noah tuck charge of de licker. So they kept goin' on and hit kept on rainin' and ev'ything was gittin' 'long easy.

"Look like shallow water ahead," Japeth holler' from de foredeck. "Ham, bring me dat soundin' line."

"Can't," say Ham. "Hit's on de main deck wid de animals, and maw told me to stay 'way from dem animals ev'y since I got de fleas on me."

"I didn't say no sich thing," Miz Noah holler. "I said de next time you played wid dat skunk

[31]

I was gonter drap you overboa'd. I ain't got de b'iler deck smellin' right yit, since de time you brang him up yar."

So while they was argyin', ker-blam! De ark struck de ground.

"No use in soundin' now," say Noah. "Us done landed. Shem, you drag de fires and dreen de b'iler. Jape, you bring me a dove. Ham, you tell yo' mammy to set de kag of licker out in de companionway, 'cause I feels my phthisic hurtin' me again."

So in due time de water went away and de ark was settin' high and dry. And all de animals wawked off and on wawked de Lawd.

"Well, Noah," say de Lawd, "did I rain or didn't I rain?"

"Lawd," say Noah, "you rained."

"He don't know did you rain, Lawd, or did you snow," say Ham. " 'Cause he was layin' up in de pilot-house, drunker'n a b'iled owl."

So dat made old Noah mad and he jumped up and cussed out Ham, hot and heavy.

"You, Noah!" say Miz Noah. "Ain't you a shame to cuss like dat in front of de Lawd!"

"Dat's all right, Sister Noah," say de Lawd. "Hit's jest natchal for a good steamboat cap'm to git mad and cuss once in a while. I never seed a good cap'm yit which wouldn't do hit, do you plage 'em. And when they kin cuss good like Noah, I don't mind hyarin' hit. I likes to hyar good cussin' same as anybody else. What I don't like to hyar is bad cussin'."

So Noah tuck his wife and his sons and they wives and got out of de ark and started peoplin' de yearth again.

The Romance and Marriage of Abraham

WELL, no sooner do de Lawd swage de flood waters and people start gittin' thick again, to they start gittin' in devilment again. Whar you find a heap of people you gonter find a heap of sin.

So about de meanest man in town was a man named Babel. He robbed de poor and he robbed de rich. He shot dice and he played seven-up.

He sinned on Sunday same as Monday. And he got drunk ev'y Sadday night and whupped his wife. So de people got sick and tired of him and told him he better mend his ways or else de sheriff would lock him up.

"De sheriff and who else?" say Babel. "He's my brother-in-law and I knows his secrets."

"Well, maybe de jedge," say de people.

"I ain't skeered of de jedge," say Babel. "Efn I told what I knows about him, he'd jest go out and hang hisself."

"Well," say de people, "you may got de sheriff and you may got de jedge. But hit's one man you ain't got."

"Who dat?" say Babel.

"De Lawd," say de folks. "And hit ain't been so long since de Lawd hauled off and flooded out bigger men den you, 'cause they was sinful."

"I ain't skeered of high water," say Babel. "Do de levee bust, I'll git on top of my house and set hit out."

"When de Lawd flood," say de people, "hit gits higher'n de top of yo' house."

"Well, hit ain't gonter git no higher'n de house which I'm gonter build," say Babel. " 'Cause I'm gonter build me a house which'll reach plum to

[35]

heaven. And do de flood git dat high, de Lawd'll git wet too."

Well, de people hadn't thought about dat, so when Babel started to buildin' his house, ev'y-body come over and went to work for him. But hit was one man, name Abraham, which wouldn't work for him.

"Better come on, Abraham," say Babel. "I'm payin' six bits a day."

"I got six bits," say Abraham.

"All right, son," say Babel. "But efn hit gits to rainin' and floodin' don't come knockin' on my door. When de flood come you might jest as well start sproutin' fins, 'cause you gonter has to do some swimmin'."

Abraham kinder got worried 'cause he wa'n't much on swimmin'. "I'll let you know quick as I turns hit over in my mind," he say. So he sot down to think and about dat time yar come de Lawd, wawkin' down de road, singin':

> "I give old Norah de rainbow sign,
> Says 'No more water, but fire next time'
> Better git a home inner dat rock,
> Don't you see?"

"Which rock is dat, Lawd?" say Abraham.

So de Lawd looked up and see hit was Abraham. "Well, dad blame my ole hide," say de Lawd, "you's de very man I been huntin' for."

"Well, hyar I is," say Abraham.

"Abraham," say de Lawd, "I'm gittin' sick and tired of de way people is carryin' on, sinnin' and gamblin' and good-timin', quick as I turns my back. I ain't never seed so much licker-drinkin' and carryin' on in all my life. I likes for mankind to enjoy theyselves, and I knows they gonter cut up a little, ev'y so often. Hit's plain natchal. But they don't know when to stop, and I'm gittin' tired of hit."

"De trouble is, Lawd," say Abraham, "hit's so many young folks since you flooded 'em out ——"

"Naw, hit ain't," say de Lawd. "Don't go to blamin' ev'ything on de young folks. Hit's old folks, too. And de trouble is, they's jest mean in they hearts. They's got bad blood."

"Old folks is purty bad, Lawd," say Abraham. "Hit's somethin' wrong."

"Well, I'm gonter change hit," say de Lawd. "I ain't gonter spend all my time tryin' to keep people goin' to church which is too mean to do me any good did they come. I'm jest gonter pick me out a good man and give him all de land he wants and keep him for my own business and let de devil git all de rest."

"Hit's a lot of good land round yar, Lawd," say Abraham.

"Dat's hit," say de Lawd. "I picks me out a good man and give de land to him, and let him and his chilluns work hit for me."

"Sounds good," say Abraham. "Efn I was a married man, I'd ax you for de job."

"Ain't you married yit?" say de Lawd.

"Nawsuh," say Abraham.

"You been sparkin' round Sarah long enough to git married about twice," say de Lawd. "What de matter? Don't you know how to handle her?"

"Hit ain't dat, Lawd," say Abraham.

"I bet hit is," say de Lawd. "You jest let dat gal git ahead of you. Son, all you got to do to a gal like Sarah is jest git you a pair of licenses and say, 'Come on.' I know dese gals which sets round and make excuses. You got to handle 'em. She'll set and make excuses to de cows come home, and all de time hopin' you gonter grab her and marry her. All you got to do is git a pair of licenses and holler, and she'll come a-runnin'."

[38]

"Well, hit ain't dat, Lawd," say Abraham. "Cou'se I ain't axed her yit. 'Cause us got to have a place to live at, when we gits married, efn she'll have me."

"She'll have you, son," say de Lawd, "and she'll be glad to git you. And she'll be glad to live anywheres you want to live."

"Dat's de p'int, Lawd," say Abraham. "Hit ain't no place to live, 'cause no matter where you lives, they makes so much noise over yonder at Babel's new house to we wouldn't have no peace of mind. Dem men workin' on Babel's house cusses and hollers and calls ev'ybody dirdy names to I'm ashame' to take a wife of mine whar she kin yar all dat kind of racket."

"Is dat a fack?" say de Lawd.

"Lawd," say Abraham, "I yared a heap of cussin' in my life, but I never yit yared such cussin' as goes on over at Babel's. Babel he cusses de supertenner and de supertenner he cusses de wawkin' bosses, and de wawkin' bosses cusses de mens, and de mens cuss de mules, to de mules is about de only thing on de job which don't do no cussin'. Why, Lawd, hit's a wawkin' boss in de brickyard which kin stand flat-footed and out-cuss ole Cap'm Cooley, rain or shine."

[39]

"Well, I be doggone," say de Lawd. "I didn't know all dat was goin' on. I guess you done right not to take Sarah over whar she kin yar all dat kind of racket."

"Yeah," say Abraham, "and when a man gits started cussin' I don't reckon even you could make 'em stop."

"And on de yuther hand," say de Lawd, "I done wrote you down for my head man, and I wants you to marry Sarah and have a heap of chilluns and grandchilluns to work dis land. And I don't want Sarah to yar all dat cussin', so I guess I might jest as well git busy and pass a miracle on dem cussin' boys."

"Gonter strike 'em dumb, is you, Lawd?" say Abraham.

"Naw, I ain't gonter strike 'em dumb," say de Lawd. "Dumb folks kin cuss on they hands. You jest watch me."

So de Lawd r'ared back and passed a miracle and say, "Let all dese cussin' boys turn into for-eigners so's when they cusses nobody can't onder-stand 'em."

So, 'bout dat time Babel started to cuss de su-pertenner and de supertenner couldn't onder-stand him. "Well," say de supertenner, "whyn't you go on and start a hand laundry, old Slant-eyes? 'Cause you looks like a Chinaman to me."

So de supertenner starts to cuss de foreman, and de foreman say, "You needn't come none er dat Eye-talian tawk on me, son. Supertenner or no, you better git you a grind organ and monkey."

So dat's de way hit was right on down de line. Some of 'em was Greeks and some was Eye-talians and some was Rooshin' and some was Franch and de rest of 'em was Gawd-knows-what. And couldn't nobody onderstand 'em whether they was cussin' or jest plain tawkin'. So purty soon they seed they wan't gittin' nowheres, so they got on a boat and went to Yurrop and they been dar ev'y since.

So Abraham he went and got a pair of licenses and wawked up to Sarah. "Git yo' bonnet, Good-lookin'," he say.

"What I want to git my bonnet for?" say Sarah.

"Well, don't git hit, den," say Abraham. "You looks jest as good to me barehaided as you does wid a bonnet."

"Aw, whyn't you go on wid dat fool tawk, Abraham," say Sarah. "You must be crazy.

You oughter not to tawk so mean, 'cause you's a big stout man and I ain't nothin' but a little gal. You makes me skeered."

"I'm gonter tawk meaner'n dat efn you don't come on," say Abraham.

"All right," say Sarah. " 'Cause I sho don't like to yar you tawk mean."

So they gits married and takes over de land, and before cotton-pickin' time hit was a baby runnin' round de house name Isaac.

Little Isaac

ABRAHAM was a man which loved de Lawd. He loved Sarah and he loved little Isaac, but they all had to git out of de way when de Lawd was in town.

"You stick by me, Abraham," say de Lawd, "and I'll stick by you, rain or shine."

"All de time, Lawd," say Abraham. "I'm wid you, rain or shine; hot or cold. Hit's all de same to me. I'm wid you."

"Dat's de way I like to hyar my people tawk," say de Lawd. "Hit's so much sin on de yearth

dese days and times to when I see a man stickin'
by me, well, I'm gonter treat him right. I'm
jest gonter give you some more land. You kin
have dat forty acres over by de creek, and dat
eighty down in de river bend, too."

"Lawd, I got a mighty heap er land, now,"
say Abraham, "and I ain't but jest one man,
you know."

"Yeah," say de Lawd. "You's jest one man,
but you's a mighty good man. You better take
dat forty on de yuther side of de creek, too. Hit
ain't much for cotton, but hit grows 'taters
mighty fine."

"Thanky, Lawd," say Abraham. "I'm kinder
land poor now, wid taxes so high. But efn you
says, well, I'll jest do de best I kin."

"Dat's de way I likes to hyar a man tawk," say
de Lawd. "You kin have dem two forties up by
de Big Road, too. And do you need some help
workin' hit, whyn't you put you' chilluns to
work?"

"I ain't got but only Isaac," say Abraham.
"And he ain't hardly big enough to wawk, yit."

"All right," say de Lawd, "and you better take
dat forty of new ground over on de ridge. Hit'll
grow cawn."

Little Isaac

So Abraham went and told Sarah.

"Sarah," he say, "hit's jest too much land for me to work."

"Yeah?" say Sarah.

"Course Isaac will be big enough to help out some er dese days," he say. "But hit's too much for me and Isaac too."

"Yeah?" say Sarah.

"I been tawkin' to de Lawd about hit," say Abraham, "and from whad de Lawd say, Isaac oughter has a few little brothers comin' along to sort of help out, too."

"Yeah?" say Sarah.

"Yeah," say Abraham.

"Well," say Sarah, "I been tawkin' to de doctor about hit, and from what de doctor say, hit seem like Isaac ain't gonter has no little brothers. And sisters, too."

"But de Lawd say," say Abraham.

"Dat's you and de Lawd," say Sarah. "De doctor say, too, and I'm bankin' on de doctor."

"I'm bankin' on de Lawd," say Abraham.

So about dat time, in wawked de Lawd. "Hy-dy Abraham! Hy-dy Sarah!" he say. "I was wawkin' down de road and I jest drapped in."

"Hit is about supper time, ain't hit?" say Sarah.

But de Lawd didn't pay her no mind. "How's farmin', Abraham?" he say.

"Lawd," say Abraham, "farmin' is plum rotten."

"Well," say de Lawd, "maybe you needs some more land. You kin have dat forty over behind de ridge, and hit's about eighty in de creek bottom on de far side er dat which you kin have."

"I'm land poor, now, Lawd," say Abraham. "I got more land den I know how to handle."

"Make yo' chilluns help you out," say de Lawd.

"I ain't got but only Isaac," say Abraham, "and from what Sarah tells me, he's de last one."

"Well, wait and let de grandchilluns help out. You gonter has a heap er grandchilluns, maybe," say de Lawd. "I wonder what Sarah is got for supper?"

"Cabbages," say Sarah, "and cawn bread."

"I don't like cabbages," say de Lawd, "nor neither cawn bread. Hit jest don't smell good. I likes to smell meat roastin'. I can't eat nothin', but I do love to smell meat roastin'. Efn hit's anything I likes to smell, hit's meat a-roastin'."

"Jest a minute, Lawd," say Abraham. "I been layin' off to do some barbecuin' for a long time. Jest wait." So Abraham went out and got him a shoat and put him on de barbecue pit and barbecued him.

"Smell like shoat," say de Lawd.

"Hit is shoat," say Abraham. "Ain't he sassy-lookin'?"

"Makes me sick to my stomach," say de Lawd.

So Abraham tuck de shoat off and kilt a calf and barbecued him.

"Smell like calf barbecuin'," say de Lawd.

"Hit's de fattest yearlin' I got," say Abraham.

"Sho do stink, don't hit?" say de Lawd.

So Abraham went out and caught a sheep and barbecued him.

"I must be crazy," say de Lawd, "but efn I got good sense, dat smell like a sheep. You don't mean to tell me you's barbecuin' a sheep, does you?"

So Abraham tuck de sheep off de fire and sot down and scratched his haid. "Lawd," he say, "dat's be best I kin do. You don't like shoat, and you don't like yearlin', and you don't like sheep. I ain't got nothin' round de house wid enough meat on hit to barbecue for you to smell.

I'm powerful sorry, but what I ain't got I jest ain't got."

"Abraham," say de Lawd, "I been settin' hyar lookin' at Isaac. He's mighty fat, ain't he?"

"Oughter be," say Abraham. "Dat boy gits de best we got. I loves him mighty nigh as good as I does you, Lawd, and I'd do mighty nigh anything for him which I would do for you."

"I been thinkin'," say de Lawd. "I jest wonder how boy meat smells."

"Lawd, what you tawkin' 'bout?" say Abraham. "Dat's my baby."

"Abraham," say de Lawd, "go out and barbecue me dat boy."

"But, Lawd," say Abraham, "dat's my onliest baby. I know you is jest funnin' wid me, now. Course I ain't gonter kill my own baby."

"Abraham," say de Lawd, "you been tellin' me what you'd do for me, ev'y since I knowed you. And I been a-listenin', and I been doin' things for you. Now hyar I axes you to do somethin' for me and you says naw. I might of knowed hit all along. You's a mighty good man, to hyar you tell hit. You'd promise to do mighty nigh anything for me, I reckons. But you jest **promise wid yo' mouf.** You's one er deseyar

mouf Christians, always tawkin' good wid yo'
mouf. But when de time come to do somethin',
you always got some excuse."

"Aw, Lawd," say Abraham, "don't be so hard
on me. You don't speck me to go out and burn
my own boy, does you? Dat ain't right, Lawd."

"I ain't got no time to listen to a mouf Christian," say de Lawd. "De on'y kind of Christian
I likes is a Christian which is a Christian wid his
heart as well as his mouf. So jest hand me my
hat so I kin git on amongst some people which
loves me."

"Lawd, I loves you," say Abraham.

"Wid yo' mouf, yeah," say de Lawd. "Mouf
Christian."

"Naw, suh, Lawd," say Abraham. "I loves
you in my heart. And I loves Isaac, too."

"Well," say de Lawd, "hit's me or Isaac."

"Lawd," say Abraham, "you's done a mighty
heap for me, and I ain't never done much for
you to pay you back. You give me what I got,
and I ain't never done nothin' but jest tell you
'thanky.' But you kinder got me up a stump.
S'posin' I goes out and roasts myse'f? I'm bigger'n Isaac, and de fire would last longer."

"And smell dem whiskers burnin'?" say de

Lawd. "I don't like to smell whiskers burnin'. Hit's worse'n rubber."

"Sarah ain't got no whiskers, Lawd. Le's burn up Sarah."

"I got my haid sot on Isaac," say de Lawd, "and when I gits my haid sot, hit ain't no use in argyin' wid me."

"Well," say Abraham, "you gived me Isaac, jest like you gived me all de rest of what I got. When things was comin' my way, I didn't argy wid you, and when things is comin' ag'in' me, I ain't got no call to argy, too. But I sho hopes you changes yo' mind about dat boy. I loves him too much."

"Isaac or nothin'," say de Lawd.

Abraham got de knife and tuck Isaac by de hand. "Come on, son," he say. So he led Isaac to de barbecue pit. "Git up on dem rocks," he say.

"Dat's whar you put de sheep, ain't hit, pappy?" say Isaac.

"Never mind de sheep," say Abraham. "Git on de rocks."

So Isaac got, and Abraham shut his eyes and raised up de knife. But about dat time some-

[50]

thin' grabbed his hand, and he looked and hit was de Lawd.

"You'll do, Abraham," say de Lawd. "I wa'n't gonter let you touch a hair on dat boy's haid. I loves dat boy better'n you does, and I got plans in my haid for him. His grandchilluns is gonter work all dis land I been givin' you. I jest wanted to make sho you was a heart Christian as well as a mouf Christian. Dat's all. I knows, now. So I'm gonter give you some more land. Hit's two forties across de road you kin have, too."

"Thanky, Lawd," say Abraham.

Mrs. Lot

WELL, Abraham and Isaac had a heap of trouble tryin' to farm all de land de Lawd gived him, so he sont and got his nephew named Lot to come and help him out. So ev'ything was goin' 'long fine to one day Miz Lot drap round to Miz Abraham's house to borry a little salt to put in de mustard greens.

"I likes a heap of salt in my greens," say Miz Lot.

"Some folks is lucky to got greens," say Miz Abraham.

"Meanin' which, Aunt Sarah?" say Miz Lot.

[52]

"Meanin' yo' chickens been gittin' in my gyarden and et up all my greenery. I and Abraham ain't had nothin' but salt meat to eat all summer."

So Miz Lot sot dar a while hummin' to herself like she ain't yared about dem chickens before, so finally she say, "I tries to keep my chickens home, Aunt Sarah, but ev'y since de shoats done et up all our cawn, they got to go somewheres to git rations."

"I didn't know you and Lot had shoats," say Miz Abraham.

"Ain't," say Miz Lot. "Hit's Uncle Abraham's shoats which et up our cawn."

So de argyment carried back and fo'th betwixt de womenfolks to finally Lot and Abraham yared de news. So Abraham sont for Lot.

"Lot," say Abraham, "I been yarin' some things about you from my womenfolks, and I reckons you been yarin' de same about me from yo' womenfolks. So I ain't sayin' who's right and I ain't sayin' who's wrong. What I'm sayin' is that life is too shawt to spend all de time argyin' betwixt de kinfolks."

"Ain't hit de truf, Uncle Abraham?" say Lot. "A man don't git to be no mo'n seven or eight hund'ed years old nohow, and hit ain't no need to spend dat time argyin' betwixt de kinfolks."

So Abraham sot down de jug and say, "Well, we might jest as well tawk hit over, Lot. Hit seem like I got shoats and you got chickens. And I plant a gyarden and you plant cawn. So dat kind of business ain't gittin' nobody nowheres. Hit's a heap er land round yar, but hit jest ain't enough to raise shoats and chickens, too. So I buys you out or you buys me out. And de one which sells, hit's onderstood he takes his hat and gits on down de road."

"Sounds fair to me," say Lot.

"Well," say Abraham, "is you buyin' or sell-in'?"

"I ain't tawked hit over wid de old lady yit," say Lot, "but de last news I yars was somethin' about de chilluns gittin' growed up and don't I think us ought to go to town and put 'em in school. So jest pay me in greenbacks, Uncle Abraham, and us'll call hit square."

So Lot tuck de money and moved his family over to a town which was name Sodom. And mean? Lawd, Lawd! Sodom was de meanest town which ever come down de pike! Ev'body in de town was mean, preachers and all.

So one day Lot's little boy come home from school and Lot say, "Well, son, whad did de teacher learn you today?"

"He learnt me better'n to try to make four passes hand-runnin'," say de little boy. "I made dat fo'th pass fair and square, too. Trey-Joe, jest as natchal as life. And de teacher said I was freezin' de dice."

"What kind of tawk is dat?" say Lot. "I ain't sont you to school to learn how to shoot dice. I sont you to school to learn yo' letters and figgers."

"Dat's what I tell de teacher," say Lot's boy. "But de teacher say ain't nobody gonter pay me to say my letters and figgers. Teacher say you got to know how to handle de dice to git along in dis man's town."

So Lot's little gal come home from school and Lot ax her what did de teacher learn her.

"Nothin'," say de little gal. "She was gonter learn us how to make love powders, but she got put in jail for killin' de preacher. So I didn't learn nothin' today. But she gonter be back tomorrow and maybe us'll learn somethin'."

"Hit's too many for me," say Lot, and he sot and sot, tryin' to figger out what he kin do bout

[55]

hit. To all at once Miz Lot come prancin' in
and ker-blam! She drug de rollin'-pin 'cross his
haid.

"Ain't I done tole you to git out and buy me
some salt?" she say.

"Watch out wid dat rollin'-pin, woman," say
Lot. "I'm gonter git yo' salt."

"Well, I want to see you move," say Miz Lot.

"Well, don't come hittin' me wid de rollin'-
pin," say Lot. "Dat ain't no way to ack round
yo' husband."

"Well, I wants some salt and I wants hit now,"
say Miz Lot.

"Well, you gonter keep messin' round me wid
dat rollin'-pin," say Lot, "and you gonter git
mo' salt den you kin handle. I'm gittin' sick and
tired of ev'y time I gits in de house you starts
hollerin' for salt. I can't no mo'n git settled
down to yar you come wantin' some salt. Now
you jest drag yo'se'f on back in de kitchen. I'll
git dat salt when I gits ready."

So about dat time, in wawked de Lawd and
Lot told him how come he was argyin' wid de
old lady.

"Yeah," say de Lawd, "dat's de way a woman
is. They don't no sooner git married to they got

to move to town to put they chilluns in school. And they don't no sooner git to town to they starts wantin' you to buy 'em somethin'. Sometimes hit's a dress and sometimes hit's a new cook-stove, and sometimes hit's sugar and sometimes hit's salt. But hit's always somethin'."

"I ain't mindin' de salt so much, Lawd," say Lot, "efn I was gittin' anywheres wid hit. But I ain't. I puts my chillun in school to learn they figgers and they learns crap-shootin'."

"And de teacher won't let us make but three passes, too, Lawd," say Lot's boy. "I made four passes and de teacher s'cused me of freezin' de dice yistiddy."

"Listen at dat," say de Lawd. "Can't make but three passes! I be doggone! Cheatin' de chilluns! What sort of people you got in dis town? Who de preacher? I wants to know how come they so low down."

"Ain't no preacher," say Lot. "He got mixed up wid a lady yistiddy and she tuck a razor to him."

"Whyn't you preach?" say de Lawd.

"And let dem boys and gals make fun of me?" say Lot. "I'm a married man, Lawd, and hit ain't never yit been a preacher in dis town which could keep de womenfolks offn him."

"They gits worser and worser de more you tells," say de Lawd.

"I was jest settin' yar studdyin' somethin' to do bout hit," say Lot, "when de old lady come in hollerin' for salt."

"Well," say de Lawd, "a man can't figger much when de womenfolks is hollerin' for salt. So hit looks like I might jest as well handle dis town myself. And from de news I yars, hit ain't nothin' shawt of fire gonter do hit much good."

"You ain't thinkin' bout broomstonin' de town, is you, Lawd?" say Lot.

"Well, I ain't sayin' what I got in my mind," say de Lawd. "All I got to say is, you better git yo' hat and de old lady and de chilluns and git on down de road. 'Cause hit's gonter be mighty hot round yar long about sundown."

"Aw, Lawd," say Miz Lot, "you ain't gonter burn dis town, is you?"

"No mind," say de Lawd. "Jest you git yo' bonnet and git goin'."

"But, Lawd," say Miz Lot, "hit's a heap of mighty fine salt round yar which ain't no need in burnin'."

"Dat's all you think about, woman?" say de Lawd. "Salt! Well I be dad burn! I bet de next time you say salt to me I'm gonter give you all de salt you wants and den some. Now git yo' bonnet and drag yo'se'f on out wid Lot and de chilluns."

So Lot and de old lady and de chilluns gits they hat and bundles and gits on down de road and de Lawd gits busy wid de broomstone. So when Lot and de family got along over de hill they looks back and sees old Sodom all lit up, a-burnin' and a-blazin'.

"Looks kind of good," say Lot, "pitchin' all dat black smoke up ag'in' de sky."

"Hit do," say Miz Lot. "But jest think of de salt goin' to waste."

"Whyn't you shut up about salt, woman?" say Lot. "You know what de Lawd said, don't you?"

But Miz Lot ain't said a word. 'Cause de minute she spoke salt wid her mouf, de Lawd passed a miracle on her and turned her into salt.

"Well," say Lot, "I reckon hit'll be some peace in de family now, 'cause I bet you ain't never gonter holler for no more salt." And she never did.

Esau

WELL, ev'ything went along mighty easy and calm and little Isaac growed up and got married and raised sheep and tuck things about as they happened. To one day the old nurse woman comed up and say, "Mister Isaac, hit's a pair of boy twins up at yo' house."

So Isaac stuck de stopper back in de jug and wiped his mouf on his sleeve. "Well, well," he say, "I guess you better name 'em Esau and Jacob. But tell de old lady de next pair of boy twins which comes along she got to name 'em herself. I don't aim to have my life worried out of me thinkin' up names for de chilluns."

So Jacob and Esau growed up, calm and easy. Jacob was a boy which got out and found him a job waterin' de stock, but Esau was a boy which tuck after his daddy. And Isaac liked Esau more'n he did Jacob.

"Whyn't you git out and go to work, Esau?" say Jacob. "You jest lays round in de shade all day, drinkin' hard licker and doin' nothin'."

"I'm helpin' my daddy," say Esau.

"And he ain't doin' nothin' but drinkin' hard licker," say Jacob. "I'm makin' me six bits a day waterin' de stock and you ain't hittin' a lick of work."

"Humph!" say Esau. "You ain't never gonter ketch me workin' for six bits a day. Look at de hairs on dat arm! Look at de hairs on dat chest! Dat's de sign I'm a stout man. I'm gonter git me a job in de circus liftin' weights."

"I ain't never seed you do no liftin'," say Jacob.

"onless hit was liftin' up a kag of licker to yo' mouf."

"Well," say Esau, "hit takes a man to lift up a kag of licker and drink outn de bunghole. You can't do hit."

So Jacob went on back to waterin' de stock and Esau went to practicin' on liftin' up licker and drinkin' outn de bunghole. And old Isaac lay back in de shade, watchin' his boys grow up in one eye and sleepin' in de yuther.

So one day de Lawd come wawkin' down de road and he seed Esau staggerin' along and singin':

> "My black gal she don't love me;
> My brown she up and quit me;
> My wife runned off wid de preacher.
> Shoot de licker to me, John!"

"What you mean by staggerin' round singin' dat John song?" say de Lawd. "You know better'n dat." But old Esau jest rocked along singin':

> "I'm goin' down to de river;
> Set right down on de levee;
> R'ar way back and holler.
> Shoot de licker to me, John!"

"I bet I better not ketch you settin' on de

levee singin' dat John song," say de Lawd. "I sho would shove you in de river, you low-down scamp, you."

"Say which, Lawd?" say Esau.

"Say, why don't you settle down and git to work like Jacob?" say de Lawd. "You been monkeyin' round yar, drinkin' and sinnin' and carryin' on to I'm plum sick of you. First thing you know you gonter be a old man and den whar you gonter be? You won't have no money and won't nobody hire you, and first thing you know you gonter be knockin' on de door at de county farm."

"Who, me?" say Esau. "And my daddy got more money'n old Jay Gould? Humph! Haw, haw, haw!" And Esau went on down de road, staggerin' and singin' de John song.

So de Lawd wawked right straight over and woke old Isaac up.

"Who's it?" say Isaac.

"Me," say de Lawd.

"Well, you hafter excuse me, Lawd," say Isaac. "My eyes ain't what they used to be."

"Yeah," say de Lawd, "hard licker sho do work on de eyes. But hit ain't no need in me tawkin' to you bout yo'se'f. I come to see you bout dat worthless low-down son of yo'n."

"Ain't he a shame, Lawd?" say Isaac. "I tawked to dat boy and I tawked to him. But hit ain't doin' no good. He jest dead sot on hangin' round old man Laban's gals all de time. I say to him, I say, 'Son, whyn't you be a man like Esau?' But he ain't payin' me no mind."

"You tawkin' bout Jacob," say de Lawd, "and me tawkin' bout Esau."

"You tawkin' bout Esau?" say Isaac.

"Yeah," say de Lawd. "I jest seed him staggerin' round, singin' de John song."

"He sings hit right well for a boy, don't he, Lawd?" say Isaac. "I learnt him dat song."

"He gonter be singin' hit on de county farm fust thing you know," say de Lawd. "I don't like his way of doin's. I likes Jacob."

"Well, Lawd," say Isaac, "I been knowin' dem boys ev'y since they was babies. And Esau is got his bad p'ints and Jacob is got his good p'ints. But give me Esau ev'y time. Esau may have licker on his mind. But Jacob is got women on his mind. And betwixt licker and women, give me licker ev'y day. Hyar me, I got old rusty money which ain't never been spent, and Jacob goes down yonder workin' for old man Laban, jest so's he kin be round his gals."

"Workin' ain't never hurt nobody," say de Lawd.

"Ain't gonter do him no good, too," say Isaac, "s'cusin' what he gittin' paid."

"What's he gittin' paid?" say de Lawd.

"You won't believe hit, Lawd, when I tells you," say Isaac, "but dat simlin-haided runt is gone down and promised to work for old man Laban seven years!"

"Well, Laban gonter pay him off, ain't he?"

"Yeah," say Isaac, "Laban gonter pay him off, but not wid money. He gonter pay him off wid a woman!"

"Naw?" say de Lawd.

"Hit's a natchal fack," say Isaac.

"Well, I be dog!" say de Lawd. "And yar I done writ down dat Jacob is gonter be my choice."

So de next day Isaac 'lowed he gonter up and give all his money and sheep and things to Esau, and Jacob yared about hit. So Jacob knocked off workin' and slipped in de house and put on buckskin gloves so he'd feel like Esau to de hands.

"Hyar's Esau, daddy," say Jacob. "Did you

[65]

said you's gonter give me some money and sheep?"

So old Isaac reach out and feel de hair on de buckskin gloves and he think hit Esau, so he gived Jacob all de money and sheep. So Jacob tuck de money and wawked round de house singin':

> "Cap'm, Cap'm, I ain't no fool,
>   Dis mawnin'!
> Cap'm, Cap'm, I ain't no fool,
>   I got more money'n ole Jay Gould,
>   Dis mawnin'!"

So Esau yared what had happened and he got mad, but he didn't let on.

"Jacob," he say, "somebody tole me you gonter git married up wid a gal name Leah."

"Somebody tole you wrong," say Jacob. "I'm gittin' married up wid Rachel."

"Yeah?" say Esau. "Well, they told me hit was Leah."

"Humph!" say Jacob. "Any time a good-lookin' man like me gits married wid a big fat cow like old Leah, you kin kick me all over town. She don't never do nothin' but stand round makin' foolish tawk and gigglin'. And ugly? Lawd, Lawd! She's pop-eyed and knock-kneed and she got two left feet and her hands ain't mates. And ain't got hardly no teeth."

"So you ain't carin' much about marryin' Leah, huh?" say Esau.

"I ain't dat crazy," say Jacob. "I might be a fool, but I ain't crazy. Rachel is de gal I got my eyes on. Good-lookin' and don't keer who likes hit. And lively? Mankind! You ain't never seed nothin' to you see dat Rachel cuttin' up."

"Is dat a fack?" say Esau. "Well, I'll drap around to de weddin'."

So when time come for de weddin', Esau was on hand all dressed up in a spike-tail coat, jest struttin' round and makin' things lively. Old Laban rolled out a kag or two of drinkin' licker to kinder git de weddin' goin', and soon as dem kags hit de ground Esau up and picked one of 'em up and drunk outn de bunghole.

"Looky yonder at de stout boy," say Rachel. "Somebody tole me old Samson was daid and I guess maybe you ain't Samson, 'cause you sho ain't daid. But you sho do swing dat kag round mighty light."

"Dat ain't nothin', baby," say Esau. "I kin set you on top of dat kag and lift you and de kag too."

[67]

So Rachel laughed at dat, and Jacob got mad. "Say," he yells, "who gonter git married round yar, Esau? Me or you?"

"I ain't tawkin' bout gittin' married," say Esau. "I'm tawkin' bout drinkin' licker outn de bunghole. Anybody kin git married, but hit takes a man to lift up a kag of licker and drink outn de bunghole."

"I kin drink outn de bunghole," say Jacob, and he ups wid de kag and strains and strains, to finally he gits a drink.

"Jacob kin drink outn de bunghole, too," say Esau.

"Naw?" say Rachel. "I got to see hit wid my own eyes before I b'lieves hit."

So Jacob lifts up de kag again and takes another drink. And about dat time old Laban come out and Rachel told him.

"Naw?" say Laban. "I don't b'lieve he kin drink outn de bunghole to I sees hit wid my own eyes."

So Jacob lifted up de kag and tuck another drink. And den first one and another come up and Esau told 'em Jacob could drink outn de bunghole and Jacob had to drink before they'd believe hit. And hit wa'n't long to Jacob was flat of his back, drunker'n a b'iled owl.

"Us better git de weddin' started before folks gits to tawkin'," say Laban. "Somebody go wake up de preacher, and, Rachel, you line up by de bridegroom."

"How come Rachel gonter line up?" say Esau.

"She got to line up to git married, ain't she?" say Laban.

"Well, she ain't gonter," say Esau. "You thinks jest 'cause my brother is drunked you kin put Rachel off on him, does you? Well, you jest try hit and you gonter yar from me. My brother comed over yar to marry Leah, and he gonter marry Leah, drunk or sober. And efn somebody got to marry Rachel, well, I'll marry her. I don't keer one way or de yuther."

"Sounds fair," say Laban. "Ev'ybody satisfied?"

"Suits me," say Rachel.

"Me, too," say Leah.

"Hit's all right wid me and Jacob," say Esau.

So when old Jacob sobered up he was married with Leah. "Well," he say, "I got more money'n old Jay Gould. But I be doggone efn hit ain't worth ev'y cent of hit."

[69]

*W*restling *Jacob*

JACOB was a man which liked to have a heap of chilluns runnin' round de house and he was de kind of man which got about ev'ything he liked. So one day old man Laban, his daddy-in-law, said, "Well, I hope you been havin' a good time at my house, and hit's gonter be kind of lonesome when you takes yo' family and leaves."

"Who say I'm leavin'?" say Jacob.

"I says you is," say Laban. "So good-by. I don't mind s'portin' a son-in-law and four or five chilluns. But hit looks like ev'y time I turns around I'm a granddaddy again."

So they argyed, and finally Laban told him he'd give him half de sheep and things efn he'd go; so Jacob tuck his half and his family and started down de road. And de fust man he met was de Lawd.

"Whar you goin', Jacob?" say de Lawd.

"I ain't decided yit," say Jacob. "Laban got to meddlin' wid my family affairs so I up and left."

"You got a right good-size family," say de Lawd. "How many chilluns you got?"

"Well, de last time I and de old lady counted 'em," say Jacob, "hit was about twelve or fifteen boys. Us quit countin' de gals."

"Un-hunh," say de Lawd. "No wonder Laban got to meddlin'. But you ain't made up yo' mind whar you goin' wid 'em?"

"I done made up his mind," say Miz Jacob. "Us is goin' and visit Esau for a while."

"Dat's quar," say de Lawd. "I was jest

[71]

tawkin' to Esau yistiddy, and he ain't yared about de visit."

"We gonter s'prise him," say Jacob.

"Well," say de Lawd, "hit ain't none er my business, but I'm remarkin' dat from de way Esau cusses and carries on ev'y time he thinks about all de money you beat him out of, hit looks like he gonter s'prise you, too, do he gits aholt of you. Ev'y time I axes him yo' name he swells up and acks like a he-coon."

"He ain't got no right to git mad at me, Lawd," say Jacob. "I cheated him outn his money, all right. But looky what he tricked me into marryin'."

"Hysh yo' mouf, **you** good-for-nothin' scound'el," say Miz Jacob. "De next time you tells de Lawd yo' family troubles I'm gonter rub yo' haid on de ground."

"Yes, darlin'," say Jacob.

"Well," say de Lawd, "I don't never monkey in family affairs, and I ain't sayin' which got tricked de worser, you or Esau. But all I got to say is, Esau ain't never had to live wid Leah and he is had to live widout dat money. And de way he figgers hit, he gonter jest about bust you open do he git his hands on you. And Esau is a stout man, too."

"Jacob ain't skeered of Esau," say Miz Jacob. "Look at dem stout arms on him."

Well, de Lawd kind of feels sorry for Jacob, so he wawks up and feels of Jacob's arms. "Purty good arms," say de Lawd. "But I b'lieve they is jest a little too soft right now. Maybe you better do some wrastlin' to git harded up before you tackles Esau. Esau is mighty hard, you know."

So Jacob runned up and down de road and chopped wood and jump de rope, but he didn't had nobody to wrastle wid. So de Lawd sont up and had a angel come down to wrastle wid Jacob.

"I'm gonter make out like you's Esau," Jacob told de angel. "So jest look out for de under holts."

"Well, efn you's gonter ack dirdy about hit," say de angel, "I'm gonter do you about like Esau would do you."

So Jacob and de angel r'ared back and circle round, slow and easy.

"When I grabs you, boy," say Jacob, "you gonter think old Satan got you."

"You better grab old Satan den me," say de angel, " 'cause old Satan wouldn't do nothin' but

[73]

jest pitch you in de fire wid a pitchfawk. And dat ain't nothin' to what I'm gonter do."

So Jacob arch his back and crook his elbows and started dancin' stiff-laiged round de angel. "When I grabs you," he say, "de yearth gonter tremble and de sky turn red. De sun'll turn cold and de water run uphill."

"Yeah," say de angel, "when you grabs me de next news anybody gonter yar, you gonter be beggin' de Lawd to come drag you out from under me."

"Well," say de Lawd, "I thought I was gonter see some wrastlin'. But hit looks like now hit ain't nothin' but a braggin' match."

"I ain't braggin'," say Jacob. "I'm tellin' him."

"Well, whyn't you show him?" say de Lawd.

So Jacob dances round again, and den ker-blip! He grabs de angel.

And no sooner do he grab de angel to ker-blap! Jacob hit de ground.

"Ole lady," say Jacob, "you better bring de liniment, 'cause I b'lieve I sprung my ankle when my foot slipped."

"Yeah," say de angel, "dem under holts I had on you'd make anybody's foot slip."

"I ain't no doctor," say de Lawd, "but efn I knows hay from oats, hit's gonter take more'n liniment before you wawks on dat laig again. 'Cause from de way you hit de ground, dat laig orter be broke. So you jest might as well bring out de crutches."

So they brang de crutches and Jacob crutched on back to his tent.

"Well," he say, "efn my own brother don't love me enough to invite me and my family to come to his house, well, we jest won't come. Dat's all. I ain't de kind of man which will go whar he ain't wanted, nohow. So I b'lieve I'm gonter settle down right yar and start me a city all by myself."

"You got a purty good start," say de Lawd. "And efn you'd stay yar you'd be all right. But you ain't."

"How come, Lawd?" say Jacob. "Dis is my land which comed from Papa Isaac, ain't hit?"

"Yeah," say de Lawd, "and yo daddy got hit from yo' granddaddy Abraham. And he got hit from me. But you ain't gonter stay."

"I don't see how come," say Jacob.

" 'Cause hit was gived to you," say de Lawd. "You worked seven years for yo' wife, and you keeps her. But you jest got dis land as a gift. I wouldn't be s'prised did I find you down in Egypt before many years."

"Naw, Lawd," say Jacob. "I'm settlin' down hyar for good."

The Fortune-Teller

ONE day old Jacob was layin' back in de shade, waitin' for de boys to come drivin' de sheep home, when he looked up and yar come de Lawd, wawkin' down de road, a-singin':

"Joseph was de smartest man you ever seen,
He wear a spotted vestment and he read yo' dream.
Onto he et de flesh down in Egypt land,
And den he wa'n't no smarter'n any yuther man.
But Joseph was a witness of his Lawd!"

"What kind of song is dat you singin', Lawd?" say Jacob.

"Dat's a prophet song," say de Lawd.

"What do hit mean?" say Jacob. "I yared you say somethin' bout dat good-for-nothin' Joseph bein' de smartest man I ever seen."

"Dat's what de song say," say de Lawd.

"I ain't aimin' to raise no argyment wid de Lawd," say Jacob, "but dat song is wrong. Joseph is about de laziest boy I got. And he ain't got sense enough to come in outer de rain."

"Is dat a fack?" say de Lawd.

"Yeah," say Jacob. "I sends him out to watch de sheep, and what do he do? Nothin' but lay back in de shade, lookin' at de sun. So I makes him go to bed early, and no quicker do I turn my back to he's out and gone. So I tells de old lady maybe he gonter be a preacher, and is out tryin' to learn all about sin so's he kin preach ag'in' it. But, naw. De old lady say she's always findin' a pack of card in his pockets, too. And dat ain't no way to learn to preach."

"All I know," say de Lawd, "is what de prophet song say, and I ain't a man which'll argy wid a song. De song say he gonter read dreams. So how's a man gonter read dreams efn he can't handle de cyards? And how he gonter read dreams efn he don't know de sun and de stars?

A man got to know cyards, and de sun and stars too, to read dreams."

"Well, maybe," say Jacob, "but I bet efn he don't grow up to be a preacher, I bet he gonter be on de chain gang."

"Well," say de Lawd, "I don't know, but I'm bettin' he ain't no preacher, and I bet he don't drag no ball and chain. Cou'se he might hold a revival ev'y now and den, and he might do a little time in jail once in a while. But I bet he don't be no preacher or no chain-gang hand as a regular thing."

So while de Lawd and Jacob was argyin' about him, Joseph was out wid de sheep. But he wa'n't payin' de sheep no mind. He was keepin' his eye on de road.

So purty soon he seed a bunch of gypsies drivin' down de road, and he got up and kilt a sheep and tuck and made stripes on his coat wid de blood. Den he got elderberries and made some more stripes and den he got some yuther yarbs and sort of spotted hit up cyourious, and by de time de gypsies got up to him he had about de stripedest coat in town.

"Hey-ho, gypsy brothers!" say Joseph. "How y'all gittin' along wid yo' work?"

"Meanin' which, Country Boy?" say de haid gypsy.

"Fawtune-tellin'?" say Joseph.

So de haid gypsy looked at de yuthers and say, "Maybe us kin grab dis boy, and his sheep, too. I'll make tawk wid him, and when I give de signal, y'all grab." And den he turn' to Joseph.

"Fawtune-tellin'," he say, "ain't so good and hit ain't so bad. How you gittin' along wid yo' sheep-herdin'?"

"Who, me?" say Joseph. "I ain't no sheep-herder. I's a fawtune-teller."

"Yeah?" say de haid gypsy. "Fawtune-teller, is you?"

"Yeah," say Joseph. "I's a fawtune-teller from away back yonder."

"I sees yo' striped coat now," say de haid gypsy. "How you gittin' along wid yo' faw-tune-tellin'?"

"Not so good and not so bad," say Joseph, tryin' to act mannish like de haid gypsy. "I been countin' on j'inin' up wid a band of y'all boys and doin' a little travelin'. What I needs is travelin'."

So de haid gypsy told de yuther gypsies they

didn't need to watch for no signal. "Well," he say to Joseph, "whyn't you j'ine our band? Hit ain't so much, but hit's better'n none."

"I don't keer efn I do," say Joseph.

"Well," say de haid gypsy, "we might jest as well herd up dese sheep. 'Cause efn they ain't yo'n, hit don't matter whose they is."

Joseph wa'n't so happy about his daddy's sheep gittin' stoled, but he didn't want to let on. So de gypsies herded up de sheep and put Joseph in a wagon and driv off. And one of de menfolks rid back to town and handed old Jacob a note which say:

"DEAR MR. JACOB: We got yo' boy name Joseph and de sheep which he's herdin'. For five hund'ed dollars you kin have de boy and de sheep. Put de money in de hollow tree. Yours truly. GYPSIES."

So Jacob leaned back and hollered: "Reuben, how many sheep did Joseph had out dis mawnin'?"

"About five hund'ed," say Reuben.

"Oh, well," say Jacob, "what's five hund'ed sheep?"

So when de gypsies didn't found de money in de hollow tree they tuck and driv on down to Egypt. And de first man they seed was old Cap'm Potiphar, wawkin' long de road wid his haid hangin' low.

"Hey-ho, Cap'm Potiphar!" say de haid gypsy. "You's lookin' kind of down in de mouf today. What de trouble?"

"No trouble a-tall," say Cap'm Potiphar. "Only I went crazy last spring and when I comed to my senses I was married wid a woman."

"Naw?" say de haid gypsy.

"Hit's a natchal fack," say Cap'm Potiphar. "And dat ain't all. She is one of deseyar kind of womens which is always got to have somebody round to play wid. Efn hit ain't de church social, hit's de fish-fry. I never seed a woman always got to go somewheres like she does."

"Whyn't you let her go?" say de haid gypsy.

"She won't go by herself," say Potiphar. "I tell her to go on by herself, and she jest sets down in de floor and bawl and squall. She got to have somebody to play wid or she won't play. I never got so tired of a woman in all my life."

"Well, whyn't you play wid her?" say de haid gypsy.

"Who, me?" say Cap'm Potiphar. "I'm a cap'm and I got to march my soldiers. I ain't got time to play wid a woman all my life. Once in a while I don't mind. But dat woman wants me round her all de time."

"Well," say de haid gypsy, "whyn't you hire somebody to play wid her while you's marchin' yo' soldiers?"

"Ev'ybody round yar knows her too well," say Cap'm Potiphar.

"I got a good-for-nothin' boy in de wagon which I hires out to you cheap," say de haid gypsy. "He's sort of crazy, but he ain't no harm. He always is monkeyin' wid 'de cyards and makin' like he's a fawtune-teller. He might kin do de job for you and not know what he's puttin' up wid."

"Sounds purty good," say Potiphar. "Trot him out."

So de haid gypsy tuck and led Joseph before Cap'm Potiphar, and Cap'm Potiphar looked him over.

"So you tells fawtunes, does you, son?" he say.

"You said hit," say Joseph.

"Well," say Cap'm Potiphar, "de old lady axed

[83]

me to find a fawtune-teller for her, so you jest git yo' hat and come on."

So Cap'm Potiphar led Joseph to de house and call Miz Potiphar. "He gonter tell yo' fawtune, Good-lookin'," he say.

So Miz Potiphar look at Joseph and den she reaches in her purse. "I better cross yo' hand wid silver, first," she say.

"No mind de silver," say Joseph. "When a lady is a good-lookin' lady like you is, I don't never charge 'em nothin'."

All about the Potiphar Scandal

WELL, efn what folks thinks had anything to
do wid hit, old Joseph would of been a crazy
man. His daddy which raised him thinks he's
crazy, and de haid gypsy which tuck him off
thinks he's crazy, and Cap'm Potiphar which
hired him thinks he's crazy. And even de Lawd
got to thinkin' he wa'n't so much.

But old Joseph wa'n't nobody's fool. Ev'y
time he'd tell Miz Potiphar's fawtune, he'd tell

her a heap of things which she didn't know herself.

"Yo' husband don't love you, gal," say Joseph.
"He got a brown-skin down de road he's stayin'
wid when he's tellin' you he's out marchin' his
soldiers."

"Yeah?" say Miz Potiphar. "How do you
know dat, son?"

"I kin see hit in yo' eyes," say Joseph. "Ev'y
time I looks in dem purty eyes of yo'n hits jest
like lookin' out de window and seein' ev'ything."

"What else kin you see?" say Miz Potiphar.

"I kin see you ain't so crazy 'bout yo' husband,
too," say Joseph.

"You sho kin see a heap," say Miz Potiphar.
"What else kin you see?"

"I kin see —— Naw, I guess I better not
tell you what I kin see now," say Joseph.

Miz Potiphar giggles. "Dat's jest de way wid
y'all menfolks," she say. "You tells a gal about
half what she want to know and den stops. Come
on, Joe, and tell me what else kin you see."

"Aw, naw," say Joseph. "You might git
mad."

"I won't git mad," say Miz Potiphar, "but I
might git mad efn you don't. And when I gits

[86]

mad I says things which might make you mad at me. And I sho don't want a big man like you mad at me, 'cause you might hit me wid dat big old fist of yo'n."

So dat's about de way things went along to Sadday night when Cap'm Potiphar come home.

"Hello, Good-lookin'!" say Cap'm Potiphar. "How you been gittin' along whilst I was marchin' my soldiers?"

"Marchin' yo' which?" say Miz Potiphar.

"My soldiers," say Cap'm Potiphar.

"Humph!" say Miz Potiphar. "Yo' soldiers."

"Well," say Cap'm Potiphar, "hit ain't no need in carryin' on like dat. I got to march my soldiers. I can't stay at home and play wid you all de time. My soldiers needs a heap of marchin'. I ought to be out marchin' 'em right now, but, naw, I comed home jest to see you. Baby, I do de best I kin. I gives you plenty of spendin' money and I hired dat fawtune-tellin' boy to tell yo' fawtunes, and now you gittin' mad 'cause I's marchin' my soldiers when you know you got to march soldiers, baby."

"Well, go on and march yo' soldiers, Country Boy," say Miz Potiphar. "I ain't sont for you."

So old Cap'm Potiphar sot and chawed on dat

[87]

awhile, tryin' to figger hit out. "Gal," he said finally, "hit ain't nothin' de matter wid you but you jest needs a whuppin', and I'm de man gonter whup you."

"You and who else?" say Miz Potiphar.

"I's enough," say Potiphar. "What you gonter do 'bout hit?"

"Me, I ain't gonter do nothin'," say Miz Potiphar. "But I knows somebody which will."

Well, old Cap'm Potiphar didn't know much about de womenfolks, but he wan't nobody's fool. So he riz up and say, right quick, "Whar's Joseph?"

So Miz Potiphar looked kind of skeered, and say: "I don't know. Maybe he gone to town. Hit's Sadday night."

"Well, I bet he's hidin' right in de house," say Cap'm Potiphar.

"He might be in de kitchen," say Miz Potiphar. "But he sho ain't hidin' in de closet. I jest looked in de closet and he sho ain't in de closet."

So Cap'm Potiphar drug Joseph outn de closet and sont him to jail on Act 1436, section 4, relative to being a dangerous and suspicious character.

And sixty days in jail was about as good as old Joseph wanted. "Hit'll give me time to settle down and quit runnin' round wid de women," he said. So he sot round de jail, practicin' his tricks and tellin' ev'ybody's fawtunes, to purty soon he told de fawtune of old King Pharaoh's butler which was in jail.

"What you in jail for?" say Joseph.

"Nothin'," say King Pharaoh's butler.

"I got 1436-ed too," say Joseph.

"I ain't even 1436," say de butler. "Old King Pharaoh look at me one day and say, 'Boy, I'm gonter put you in jail.' And I say, 'What about, Yo' Majesty?' And he say, 'About a hund'ed years.' And so yar I am."

"Somethin' quar bout dat," say Joseph. "Lemme see yo' hand and see what I kin see."

So Joseph read de butler's hand. "Old King Pharaoh's jest playin' wid you," he say. "Come tomorrow mawnin' he gonter send for you and make you come and buttle for him some more."

So old King Pharaoh's butcher was in jail, jest like de butler. So de butcher stuck out his hand and say, "Read dat and see what he done to me."

"Old King Pharaoh is playin' wid you, too,"

say Joseph. "But he ain't done playin' wid you yit."

"Naw?" say de butcher. "What else he gonter play about?"

"He gonter play like you's a snake," say Joseph, "and he gonter take you out and chop yo' haid off and feed you to de buzzards."

"I don't see no fun in playin' like dat," say de butcher.

"Hit's all accordin' to who playin' de buzzard bait," say Joseph.

So things turned out jest like Joseph say, and old King Pharaoh yared de news and he sont for Joseph.

"Joseph," say old King Pharaoh, "you must know a heap."

"Not so much, old King Pharaoh, Yo' Majesty," say Joseph. "But I knows a few things. I knows what you gonter do."

"Well," say old King Pharaoh, "anybody which knows what I'm gonter do knows a heap mo'n me. 'Cause I don't know, myself, half de time."

"Well," say Joseph, "you got in mind right now about makin' me yo' haid man, ain't you?"

"Dat's a fack," say Pharaoh.

"Well," say Joseph, "I'll be yo' haid man, and tell you all de news about ev'ything. But I'm warnin' you. Some of hit'll be good news and some gonter be bad news, too."

"Hit always is," say old King Pharaoh, "and I wants to yar de good news and de bad news alike. And I b'lieve you's de man which will tell me. So I'm gonter give you a robe and a ring, and a coach-and-four, and next to me you's de haid man in dis town."

So hit wan't long to de Lawd yared what had happened to Joseph down in Egypt and he went straight and told old Jacob de news.

"You 'members dat song I was singin' bout Joseph readin' dreams?" say de Lawd.

"Yeah," say Jacob. "What about hit?"

"Hit's come to pass," say de Lawd. "Joseph is de king-pin right next to old King Pharaoh hisself. Got a fine house and a good-lookin' woman and rides around town jest doggin' hit on to you wouldn't hardly b'lieve hit's de same man."

"Is dat a fack?" say Jacob. "I always knowed dat boy had somethin' in him. I used to tell de old lady all de time he was gonter turn up big some of these days."

"Well, he's sho big now," say de Lawd.

"I'm mighty proud, but I ain't s'prised," say Jacob. "I think I'll gather up de old lady and de chilluns and go down to Egypt and visit wid him a little."

Old King Pharaoh's Daughter

WELL, Jacob was a man which had a heap of chilluns. And hit seem like from Jacob on de habit kind of runned in de family. 'Cause all of Jacob's chilluns had a heap of chilluns and they chilluns had a heap more, and hit wa'n't long after they got in Egypt to hit was as many of Jacob's chilluns and grandchilluns as they was regular people in Egypt.

So when old King Pharaoh died hit was a new King Pharaoh which knowed not Joseph. So one day he sont for de sheriff.

"Sheriff," he say, "how'd de election go yistiddy?"

"Humph!" say de sheriff. "How you reckon hit went, King Pharaoh?"

"How?" say Pharaoh.

"Hebrew, mighty nigh solid," say de sheriff, "wid some country districts not yared from yit, too."

"What de matter our boys ain't out votin'?" say King Pharaoh.

"Our boys votes strong," say de sheriff. "Four or five times apiece. But dat ain't enough when de Hebrew boys votes jest once."

"You de sheriff, ain't you?" say Pharaoh. "Whyn't you granddaddy-clause dem Hebrew boys?"

"I did," say de sheriff, "but dem boys don't only kin tell you who they granddaddy is, but they kin tell you who they granddaddy's granddaddy is."

"Can't you Jim Crow 'em?" say King Pharaoh.

"Not me," say de sheriff, "not when hit comes to votin'. De last man Jim Crowed 'em and Uncle Sam got him draggin' a ball and chain."

"Well," say old King Pharaoh, "de trouble wid dem Hebrew boys is they has too many chilluns runnin' round de house. Maybe did you work 'em hard and not pay 'em, they'd git tired of buyin' shoes for de chilluns."

"Old King Pharaoh, Yo' Majesty," say de sheriff, "I been workin' dem boys to hit's a sin and a shame, and ain't paid 'em nothin' yit, but dat don't cut no ice. They makes they chilluns go barefooted."

"Well, hit ain't but one thing left," say old King Pharaoh. "I got to pass me a law dat ev'y Hebrew boy baby which is bawn is gonter git his haid chopped off."

"Hit sounds like a good law," say de sheriff, "but I bet hit ain't gonter keep 'em from bein' bawn, good law or no."

"No mind," say King Pharaoh. "Hit'll keep 'em from votin'. I bet de first man which tries to vote wid his haid cut off, hit'll be some tall doin's round election times."

Well, when King Pharaoh started choppin' de haids offn de Hebrew babies, dat made de Lawd mad. De Lawd ain't a man to monkey round in nobody's business. And he ain't a man which is gonter let somebody monkey round in his business, too. And de Hebrew chilluns was his business, 'cause they was de chilluns of de chilluns of old Abraham which de Lawd picked out for his haid man, away back yonder.

"Ain't nobody kin cut my chilluns' haids off and not yar from me," say de Lawd. So he got his hat and went down to Egypt. But when he got to Egypt things had changed mightily wid his chilluns. Times was when he could wawk up to any of his chilluns and start tawkin' to 'em, and de chilluns would know who they was tawkin' to. But workin' so hard down in Egypt and growin' up and gittin' married so fast and raisin' so many chilluns, they'd sort of forgot about de Lawd.

"I got to work me a trick on my own chilluns," say de Lawd. "So I jest might as well git started, 'cause hit's gonter take a mighty long time."

So de Lawd wawked up to a Hebrew woman wid a baby.

"Dat's a mighty purty baby you got, lady," say de Lawd.

"Yeah," say de lady. "I guess you is runnin' for sheriff or jedge, ain't you?"

"I ain't runnin' for nothin'," say de Lawd. "What dat purty baby's name?"

"Moses," say de lady.

[96]

"I bet hit's a boy baby," say de Lawd.

"Nawp," say de lady. "Hit's a gal baby."

So de Lawd studied and studied, and finally he got a idea. "Lady," he say, "I knows dat's a boy baby, 'cause I ain't never yet yared of a gal named Moses. And you's tellin' me hit's a gal 'cause you think I'm on Pharaoh's side."

"Ain't you?" say de lady.

"I'm on my own side, lady," say de Lawd. "I'm de Lawd. I'm sick and tired of de way Pharaoh been treatin' my chilluns and I come to help 'em out."

"Well," say de lady, "I ain't never yared tell of you, but you got a honest face. What do you want?"

"I wants Moses," say de Lawd. "I'm gonter work a trick."

"Guess you might as well take him," say de woman. " 'Cause efn you don't, old King Pharaoh will."

So de Lawd tuck little Moses and put him in a basket and told de baby's little sister to hide him in de bulrushes and watch him.

"You jest set and sing," say de Lawd, "and I'll do de rest."

"What must I sing, Lawd?" say de gal.

[97]

"Soap-and-water song," say de Lawd.

"Dat ain't no nice song," say de gal.

"Well, ain't nobody gonter yar you," say de Lawd.

So Moses' little sister sot down on de river-bank singin':

> "Poor little baby, layin' in de sand,
>   R'ar back and holler like a natchal man.
>   Soap and water, sho git yo' dirdy self clean."

So 'bout dat time old King Pharaoh's daughter was comin' down to de river to go swimmin' and she yared de gal singin'.

"Well, I be doggone!" say old King Pharaoh's daughter. "Listen at dat little Hebrew gal singin' de soap-and-water song jest like a grown woman. Where you learnt dat song at, honey?"

"No mind where I learnt hit at," say de gal. "You yared me singin', didn't you?"

"I yared you," say Pharaoh's daughter, "but I don't see no baby playin' in de sand."

"Hit's a heap of things you don't see, old King Pharaoh's daughter," say de gal.

So about dat time de Lawd wawks up and pinches little Moses and Moses let out a yip. So dat tickled old King Pharaoh's daughter.

"He sho do holler like a natchal man," she say. "I bet I'm gonter take dat baby home wid me and has some fun." So she tuck Moses on home, and de little sister started cryin', but de Lawd shushed her.

"Dat's part of de trick I'm workin'," say de Lawd.

Well, soon as Pharaoh yared de baby squallin' in de palace he put on his crown and roared and thundered. "Who brang a baby to my palace?" he hollered. So de sheriff wawks over and whispers in his yar and he say, "Well, I guess de less racket I makes about hit de better hit will be for ev'ybody."

So Moses stayed at de palace and acted jest like old King Pharaoh was his granddaddy. He didn't do no work and he cut up scand'lous, 'cause old King Pharaoh would keep him out of jail. To first thing anybody knowed, he was totin' a pistol.

"I ain't sayin' a word," say old King Pharaoh. "I told his maw to look out, but she wouldn't. Now efn her boy gits in devilment wid dat gun, hit's jest him and de jedge. I ain't sayin' a word, one way or de yuther."

So sho nuff, hit wa'n't long to Moses done up

and kilt a man wid de pistol, and when he seed he wa'n't gonter git Pharaoh to go on his bonds he up and left de county.

So when Moses' maw, which was de Hebrew woman, yared de news she went straight to de Lawd.

"You see what happened to my baby, don't you, Lawd?" she say.

"Do I sees?" says de Lawd. "Why, woman, I made hit happen!"

"Well," say de woman, "efn I'd 'a' raised dat boy he never would of got in dat trouble."

"Naw," say de Lawd, "efn you'd 'a' raised him Pharaoh'd had his haid chopped off. Now you jest go on, lady, and leave me tend to my own business."

"But he didn't had no business wid de pistol," say de woman.

"Dat's part of my trick," say de Lawd. "Old King Pharaoh is gonter be a hard man to trick, and hit's gonter take a mighty long time. So I'm jest takin' my time. I been workin' dis trick on him mighty nigh twenty years already, and hit ain't hardly started yit. Pharaoh's a hard man to trick and I got to take my time."

The Romance and Education of Moses

WELL, when Moses cut de county after killin' de man in Egypt he sot down by a well to rest. And about dat time yar come a good-lookin' gal drivin' some sheep down to de well to drink.

"Hy-dy, Good-lookin'!" say Moses.

"You must be tawkin' to yo'self," say de gal. " 'Cause I know you ain't crazy enough to tawk to me like dat."

"Wait and lemme help you water dem sheep," say Moses.

"I ain't crippled," say de gal. "Ev'y drummer which comes along dis way makes like he wants to help me water my sheep. You thinks jest 'cause I's a country gal I don't know nothin'. But I knows enough to keep away from all dese-yar drummers."

"I ain't no drummer," say Moses.

"I ain't carin' what you is," say de gal. "I ain't got no time to tawk wid you."

"You sho is hard-hearted to be so purty," say Moses. "But I guess dat's de way wid all purty gals. They got a heart like a rock."

"I wish hit was a rock," say de gal. "I needs a hard heart to keep a good-lookin' man like you from bustin' hit open."

So they sot around and tawked awhile to all at once yar come a man drivin' some sheep up to de well. And he runned away de gal's sheep so's his own could drink.

"How you git like that, Country Boy?" say Moses. "Whyn't you let dis lady's sheep alone?"

"Who you tawkin' to, son?" say de man. "Tryin' to show off before old man Jethro's gal, ain't you? You ain't de first city boy I ever seed tawkin' wid his mouf. You simlin-haided baboon! You jest make me mad and I'll rub yo̅ haid on de ground."

"You and who else?" say Moses.

So Moses and de man fit and Moses whupped him all over de place.

"You sho is a stout man," say Jethro's daughter. "Soon as I seed you bust dat big scound'el on de ground, I say, 'Well, dat's jest de way he kin bust my heart, too, any time he gits ready'."

So Moses and de gal got married up and Moses got a job herdin' de sheep for old man Jethro. And hit was all a part of de Lawd's trick which he was trickin' on old King Pharaoh, but Moses didn't know hit.

So one day when Moses was out herdin' de sheep, de Lawd come wawkin' up.

"Moses," say de Lawd, "you done settle down some, so I'm gonter learn you some tricks."

"You and who else?" say Moses. "De last country boy which tried to learn me some tricks ain't out of bed yit. What kind of tricks you want to learn me?"

So de Lawd seed Moses didn't know who he was, so he didn't said a word. He jest faded out, right in front of Moses. And den all at once Moses seed a burnin' bush.

[103]

"Hyar I is in de fire," say de Lawd, "but you can't see me to you pull off yo' shoes."

So Moses looked and he couldn't see nothin' but fire and smoke. Den he pulled off his shoes and dar stood de Lawd.

"Dat's a good trick," say Moses. "What's yo' name?"

"I's de Lawd," say de Lawd. "I sees all and I knows all. And I got business wid you."

"So you's de Lawd, is you?" say Moses. "I used to yar some of de old Hebrew mens tawkin' 'bout you a little."

"Yeah," say de Lawd. "De Hebrews is my chilluns and dat's de business I got wid you. I'm sick and tired of de way old King Pharaoh is doin' my chilluns. He's makin' slaves outn 'em jest like they ain't got nothin'. And my chilluns is got more land den old Jay Gould, over cross Jurdin. And what I wants you to do is lead 'em to de land. I promise' 'em de land and I'm gonter give it to 'em."

"I speck I better stay out of Egypt, Lawd," say Moses.

"Dat's all right," say de Lawd. "They got a new sheriff, now."

[104]

"But s'posin' old King Pharaoh won't let de Hebrews go?" say Moses.

"Dat's jest whar de trick comes in," say de Lawd. "You see dis wawkin'-stick? Well, hit ain't a wawkin'-stick. Hit's a trick rod. Now you jest take hit in yo' hands and lay hit on de ground twarg de east."

So Moses laid hit down twarg de east and hit turned to a snake.

"Doggone!" say Moses. "How'd I did dat?"

"Hit's all in de way you lays hit down," say de Lawd. "Now when you picks hit up, pinch de snake's tail." And Moses did and de snake turned back to de trick rod.

"Dat's a good trick," say Moses. "I'm gonter see kin I do dat again." So he done hit jest like de Lawd showed him.

"Learn me some more tricks, Lawd," say Moses.

"Stick yo' hand in yo' bosum," say de Lawd, and Moses stuck.

"Now hit's got de leprosy all over hit," say de Lawd.

"Naw?" say Moses.

"Hit's a fack," say de Lawd. "Now pull hit outer yo' bosum," say de Lawd. And Moses pulled. "Now hit's done well again," say de Lawd. And sho nuff hit was well again.

"Well, dad blame!" say Moses. "Now show me how to do dat fire trick."

"Not yit," say de Lawd. "You might burn somethin' up. But I'm gonter show you a heap of tricks before I sends you down to trick old King Pharaoh."

So Moses and de Lawd sot out on de hillside ev'y day, learnin' tricks and practicin' on ways to git de Hebrew chilluns outn Egypt.

"Lawd," say Moses, "whyn't you go down and lead de Hebrews outn Egypt?"

"Not me," say de Lawd. "I don't like Pharaoh's way of doin' things, and he might make me mad. And did I git mad and forgit myself and wave my hand jest once at him, I'd jest natchally blot out hyar and now and start off with hyarafter. I jest couldn't hold myself back, did I git mad at him. So I'm learnin' you some tricks so's you kin git jest as mad as you want to, but you won't know enough tricks to wipe out hyar and now. Wid all de tricks I'm learnin' you, you kin deal him a heap of misery, but you can't do no damage much."

"Well," say Moses, "efn you'll jest stick by me,

you jest watch old Pharaoh and me go round and round."

"I'm stickin' by you all de time," say de Lawd.

So Moses went down to Egypt and passed de word round dat he's a trick man, jest like de Lawd told him to. And all de time Moses was passin' de word, de Lawd was settin' back, eggin' him on and laughin'.

"Old King Pharaoh is a mighty smart man," say de Lawd. "But what Moses don't do to him, I'm gonter. And den whar'll Pharaoh be at?"

The Trick Boys

WELL, one day old King Pharaoh was layin' back on his throne watchin' all his trick boys do tricks.

"De next man I sees pull a rabbit outn a hat," say old King Pharaoh, "I'm gonter chop his haid off and see kin he trick hit back on his shoulders. I'm sick and tired of de same old tricks over and over again. Now I want to see some tricks, and I don't mean pullin' de rabbits outn de hats and pullin' de jacks outn de deck. I mean I want to see some sho-nuff tricks."

"Old King Pharaoh," say de haid tricker, "us is countin' on sawin' a gal in two and puttin' her back next Sadday."

"Y'all been sawin' dat gal in two and puttin' her back ev'y Sadday since y'all been trickin' for me," say Pharaoh.

"Well," say de haid tricker, "next Chuesday ——"

"Yeah, I knows," say King Pharaoh, "next Chuesday you's countin' on gittin' locked up in de cedar chist and gittin' out again. I been seein' dat trick on Chuesday ev'y since old Hector was a puppy."

"Well, Yo' Majesty," say de haid tricker, "trickin' is our business, and we does all de tricks anybody else does and a heap they don't. Efn you don't like our tricks you jest don't like tricks, and dat's all they is to hit."

So 'bout dat time yar come Moses, twirlin' his trick rod like a wawkin'-stick. So when he got up in front of King Pharaoh he jest sort of drap his wawkin'-stick careless-like, and hit turned to a snake.

"Look at dat fool wawkin'-stick, now," say Moses. "Hit oughter know better'n to carry on like dat in front of old King Pharaoh. Come

[109]

back yar, sir! Ain't I learnt you better'n to turn to a snake in front of King Pharaoh?" So he reached down and pinched de snake's tail and hit turned back to de trick rod.

"Le's see kin you do dat again," say King Pharaoh.

"Do which?" say Moses.

"Dat snake trick," say King Pharaoh.

"Dat ain't much trick," say Moses. "Anybody kin do dat." And he put de trick rod down again, and den he pinch de snake's tail. "Hit's too easy," he say.

"Lemme see kin I," say Pharaoh, and he tried hit, but he missed hit. "Doggone de luck!" he say. "I mighty nigh had hit. Lemme see you do hit again."

So Moses sort of turn round and shet bofe eyes and drap de rod over his shoulder, and hit turn to a snake. Den he reach betwixt his laigs and pinch de snake's tail and hit turned back to de rod.

"Dat settles hit," say King Pharaoh. "You's hired and dese yuther boys is fired."

"Hired for which?" say Moses.

"My tricker," say King Pharaoh.

"Not me," say Moses. "I got a job."

"Doin' which?" say Pharaoh.

"Leadin' de Hebrew boys from Egypt to de Promise' Land," say Moses.

"Is dat a fack?" say Pharaoh. "I ain't yared nothin' 'bout de Hebrew boys leavin' Egypt yit. Seems like de last news I yared from dem they was out makin' bricks for me."

"Well," say Moses, "de next news you gonter yar, they's gonter be done quit makin' bricks and headin' for de Promise' Land, right behind me and de Lawd."

"Well," say Pharaoh, "I'm de king round yar and what I says goes. And I got my mind made up on havin' me a heap of brick."

"I ain't argyin' 'bout dat," say Moses. "But all I got to say is before me and de Lawd git's done wid you, we gonter change yo' mind."

"Soap and water, Country Boy," say King Pharaoh. "Soap and water."

So Moses jest p'inted his rod at de sky and say, "Arise and turn dis water into blood." And all de water turned to blood.

"I don't drink water," say King Pharaoh.

"Wait to you look at yo' licker and see what you been drinkin'," say Moses, and he wawked on off.

So purty soon King Pharaoh got thirsty and he sont for Moses.

"Moses," he say, "I was jest foolin' wid you."

"Yeah?" say Moses. "Well, I wa'n't foolin' wid you."

"Turn dis stuff back to water," say Pharaoh, "and you kin take de Hebrew chilluns to de Promise' Land."

So Moses turned hit back to water and Pharaoh got a big drink. "Yeah," he say, "I was foolin' you—'bout lettin' you take de Hebrews."

So Moses jest lifted up his rod again and say:

"Frogs in de mill-pond,
Frogs in de clover.
Frogs in de 'tater patch,
Frogs all over."

And de frogs got into ev'ything. They got in Pharaoh's house and his shoes and his bed and his vittles, to finally all you had to do to make King Pharaoh mad was jest say "frog" at him.

"Git shut er deseyar frogs," King Pharaoh tell Moses, "and you kin lead de Hebrews to King-dom Come efn you wants to."

So Moses called off de frogs, and no quicker did all de frogs go way to old King Pharaoh crawfished about lettin' de Hebrews go. So

Moses waved his rod again, and de next minute old Pharaoh was scratchin' de gray-backs. But hit was de same old tale. Quick as Moses tuck 'em away, Pharaoh change' his mind again. So Moses kept on bringin' plague after plague. But hit was de same old story. To finally one day Moses got mad.

"King Pharaoh," say Moses, "I been monkeyin' round wid you a mighty long time, doin' a trick and undoin' hit. And you been settin' round lyin' to me about lettin' de Hebrew chilluns go. Now I'm sick and tired of yo' lyin'."

"I ain't lyin'," say Pharaoh. "I'm trickin', too. You been trickin' me and I been trickin' you."

"Well," say Moses, "I got one more trick up my sleeve, which I didn't aim to work on you onless I had to. 'Cause when I does hit, I can't ondo hit."

"Work hit," say Pharaoh, "and I'll trick you right back."

"You don't know what de trick is," say Moses.

"I ain't carin' what hit is," say Pharaoh.

"Well," say Moses, "I hates to work dis trick, 'cause you don't b'lieve me about hit."

"I b'lieves what you say about yo' tricks," say Pharaoh. "You got a heap of tricks, and they's good tricks, too. Only, they gits lice and flies and sores all over de people. But they's good tricks. You's a tricker, Moses. You's a good tricker. But I kin outtrick you. Dat's all."

"Hit ain't only I which is gonter work dis trick," say Moses. "Hit's I and de Lawd."

"I kin outtrick you and de Lawd, too," say King Pharaoh.

"Now you jest done put yo' foot in yo' mouf, old King Pharaoh," say Moses. "You been mean to de Lawd's people and de Lawd been easy on you. You work his menfolks to death and you chop his babies' haids off. And de Lawd let you off 'cause you don't know no better. But now you got to braggin' dat you's better'n de Lawd, and dat's too many."

"You tawk's like a preacher," say Pharaoh, "and I never did like to yar preachers tawk."

"You ain't gonter like hit when I strikes down de oldest boy in ev'y one of yo' people's houses, too," say Moses. "But dat's jest what I'm gonter do."

"Now you's quit trickin' and gone to lyin'," say King Pharaoh. " 'Cause when hit comes to strikin' folks down, I'm de king and I'm de only man which can do that. You's a good tricker, Moses, but you ain't a good liar."

"No mind," say Moses. "Efn you don't let de Hebrew chilluns 'go today I'm gonter strike down de oldest chilluns of yo' people. And efn you don't let 'em go tomorrow, I'm gonter strike down de next oldest. And I ain't gonter stop to you lets 'em go, efn I has to strike down all of yo' people."

"Soap and water, Moses," say Pharaoh. "Soap and water."

So Moses went out and axed de Lawd how about hit.

"You made yo' say-so like a man, Moses," say de Lawd, "and I'm right by you all de time."

So Moses went out and waved his rod and said like seven peals of thunder: "Hebrew people, kill a lamb and put de blood on your front door so the Angel of Death shall pass."

And so when it got dark, a tall black Angel of Death rode all over Egypt, into each house where de blood of de lamb was not, and he struck down de oldest son. And de next morning hit was a mighty moaning and groaning, for de Egyptian fathers and mothers saw they first-born still in death! Even Pharaoh's first-born was struck down. So Pharaoh come to Moses.

"Moses," he said, "I'm King Pharaoh, but I'm a man. I saw my baby still in death."

"And you gonter see his brother de same way tomorrow," said Moses, "unless you let my people go."

"One is too many," said Pharaoh. "I'm a man. Take yo' people and go."

"Don't try to change yo' mind, Pharaoh," say Moses, " 'cause you done tried de patience of de Lawd already. Long as hit was only me, you was safe. But you tried de patience of de Lawd. And hit wouldn't work."

The Manna of the Lord

WELL, old King Pharaoh lied to Moses but he couldn't lie to de Lawd. So soon as he comed up and told de Hebrew chilluns they could go to de Promise' Land, Moses told 'em to git they hats and line up.

"Follow me," say Moses.

"We's wid you," say de Hebrew chilluns. And off they marched, wid Moses leadin' de Hebrew chilluns and de Lawd leadin' Moses.

"I'm gonter ride on a cloud, Moses," say de

Lawd. "You jest follow dat cloud, and efn you needs me holler."

So they wawked and wawked, down de road, up de hills, and down de hollows, to finally, when hit got about sundown, they hit de Big Woods. And den de chilluns started cryin' and de womenfolks started grumblin' and de menfolks started growlin'.

"I'm hongry," say a Hebrew man. "Makin' bricks is hard work, but wawkin' down de road ain't no easier."

"Yeah," say another man, "and whatever you got to say ag'in' old King Pharaoh's brick-makin' job, you got fed. You can't say old King Pharaoh didn't feed you."

"Feed you?" say de first man. "Lawd, Lawd! Remember how dem beans and onions used to smell 'long about quittin' time? And de cawn bread and turnip greens?"

"Shut yo' mouf," say de yuther man. "Tawkin' 'bout dem beans and turnip greens and me so hongry I kin eat de shoe leather offn my shoes, right now."

So Moses yared de grumblin', but he didn't had no rations along, so he holler for de Lawd.

"Lawd," say Moses, "hit's gittin' about time to cook and eat again, ain't hit, Lawd?"

So de Lawd stuck his haid out from behind de cloud. "Well," say de Lawd, "efn yo' appetites calls for supper, jest set down under de trees."

So ev'ybody set down under de trees and waited. But didn't nothin' happen. And purty soon de menfolks started grumblin' again. So up wawked de Lawd.

"I ain't yared nothin' but grumblin' outer y'all boys, all day long," he say. "What you grumblin' 'bout now?"

"We's hongry, Lawd," say a Hebrew man.

"Well," say de Lawd, "didn't I said I'm takin' keer of y'all? When I says I takes keer of a man, I takes keer of him, and he don't has to worry. I'm gonter take keer of you, but I'm gonter do hit like I wants to and when I wants to. Hit's de way I does things."

"I know, Lawd," say de man, "but when yo' stummick gits to wroppin' round yo' back bone, you ain't payin' much mind to what folks says. Seems like when my stummick gits empty I forgits ev'ything exceptin' how good beans and onions tastes."

"Well," say de Lawd, "do you want to eat?"

"Do I want to eat?" say de man. "Lawd, I'm tellin' you plain, I'd druther eat a good mess of vittles right now den wake up in de Promise' Land tomorrow mawnin'."

"So you wants to eat," say de Lawd, "but you ain't doin' nothin' 'bout hit but jest grumblin' and growlin'. Dat ain't gonter fill yo' stummick."

"Lawd," say de man, "I'd do mighty nigh anything I knowed how to do, jest to git somethin' to eat."

"Well," say de Lawd, "answer me a question, den. What kind of a tree is dat you settin' under? What kind of trees is all over dese woods?"

So de man looked at de tree and he looked at de Lawd and grinned.

"Hit's a psaltree," he say.

"Cou'se hit's a psaltree," say de Lawd.

"And loaded down wid psalnuts," say de man.

"Sho hit is," say de Lawd. "Dat's how come I marched y'all round dis way, so's y'all could eat psalnuts for supper."

"Hod-d-mighty!" say de man. "Watch me climb up and git me a bait of psalnuts!"

"Stay outn dat psaltree," say de Lawd. "De

fust man I ketches up my psaltrees, I'm gonter
set de yaller jackets on him. Hit's a part of what
I got in my mind dat y'all got to stay outer my
psaltrees. I don't never want nobody to climb
up one of my psaltrees."

"But how we gonter git de psalnuts, Lawd?"
say de man.

"Hit's a certain manner I got in mind," say
de Lawd. So he backs up and blows like a wind
and blowed de psalnuts down. And soon as
enough was down for supper, de Lawd quit
blowin'. "Dat's de manner y'all gonter git yo'
grub ev'y day," say de Lawd. "De trouble wid
y'all is dat you don't know how to take yo' time.
And dat's what I got to learn you first. You
don't do no thinkin', but quick as somebody gits
a idea, you starts out like a bunch of sheep. And
dat ain't no way to do. You got to learn to take
yo' time. And I'm gonter march y'all round de
wilderness to you learns."

"Well," say Moses, "efn you keeps dese boys
out yar to they learns how to take they time, you
gonter keep 'em out yar a couple of years, I
reckon."

"Hit figgers down to about fawty years," say

de Lawd, "s'cusin' how old and sot in they ways, some of 'em is."

"Dat's a mighty long time," say Moses.

"And they's mighty sot in they ways, too," say de Lawd. "I got to go out and build a fire for 'em right now. I'd druther build hit myself tonight den to monkey round tryin' to learn 'em how."

So de Lawd went and built a fire and put 'em all to bed. "Y'all is mighty good chilluns," he say, "and you's mighty happy now, warm and full of psalnuts. Now see kin you remember about dis, tomorrow, when I gits y'all strung out on de road, marchin' again."

"We won't forgit, Lawd," say de Hebrew chilluns. "We knows de Lawd is gonter look out for us, 'cause we's on de Lawd's side."

"Well, dat's a mighty purty speech," say de Lawd, "but I bet my bottom dollar you changes yo' chune about de time Old Sol gits to bearin' down on you."

The Understanding

WELL, old Moses had a purty easy time leadin' de Hebrew chilluns round de wilderness. They was gittin' plenty to eat and plenty to drink and a warm fire to sleep by ev'y night. And as long as a man gits all dat he ain't gonter do much grumblin'. But some folks gonter grumble, no matter what they got. And hit was some bawn grumblers 'mongst de Hebrews.

"Remember how us used to good-time back in old Egypt?" say one of de Hebrew men.

"Yeah," say another Hebrew man. "Dem was de good old days. Didn't had to march all day and sleep on de ground all night. All you had to do was git out and make a few brick, and den go home and good-time to de cows come home!"

"Old King Pharaoh had his bad side, jest like ev'ybody else," say de first man. "But he wa'n't so bad. I wish I was back whar he is."

So dat's de way de tawk run along amongst de Hebrews. To one day de Lawd started singin' over behind his cloud:

"Oh, de Red Sea water is bitter as a gall
  And de Hebrew chilluns can't drink hit a-tall,
  But Pharaoh's army got drownded."

"Listen at de Lawd settin' over yonder singin' riddles at me," say Moses. "I ain't got no time to play riddles. I got to lead de Hebrew chilluns to de Promise' Land."

So de Lawd kept right on singin':

"Oh, de Red Sea water is deep and wide,
  And how you gonter git on de yuther side?
  But Pharaoh's army got drownded."

"I ain't studdin' de Red Sea," say Moses, "nor neither old Pharaoh's army. I's leadin' de Hebrew chilluns." So he marched right on. To all at once he comed out of de woods to a mighty wide piece of water.

"Look like de levee busted," say Moses, "and de back water backed up in de woods." So he scoop some up in his hands to git a drink, but he spit hit out right quick. "Whew!" he say, "dat's as bitter as a gall."

So de yuther Hebrews tried to drink it, but hit wouldn't go down. Den de babies started squallin' and de womenfolks started grumblin' and de menfolks started growlin'. "Us is thirsty," they say, "and dis water ain't fittin to drink."

"I'm thirsty, too," say Moses, "but I ain't no rain-maker."

"De water down in Egypt didn't taste like dis," say a man. "And efn you ain't a rain-maker you better learn how. 'Cause you led us out yar, and hit's up to you to give us some drinkin'-water."

"And s'posin' I don't?" say Moses.

"Well," say de man, "us used to put straw in our bricks down in Egypt. But hit ain't no straw out yar, so in case us tuck a notion to make some bricks we might has to use yo' whiskers instid of straw."

So Moses went and told de Lawd. "Dem boys is thirsty," he say, "and when a man gits thirsty he gits mean. I don't blame 'em much. I's kinder thirsty too, Lawd."

"Well," say de Lawd, "what dat you got in yo' hand?"

"My trick rod," say Moses.

"Well," say de Lawd, "go out and smite a rock wid hit and see don't some water come out. I thought I learnt you dat trick way back yonder."

"You did, Lawd," say Moses, "but I guess I forgot hit."

So Moses smit a rock and watered de Hebrew chilluns. But they wa'n't satisfied. They 'lowed they was sick and tired of marchin' and they'd druther make bricks in Egypt.

"Us is goin' back," say de Hebrews.

So about dat time hit was a mighty rumblin' and a mighty roarin'. And ev'ybody looked back, and yar come old King Pharaoh's army wid all de horses and chariots and soldiers and ev'y-thing, lickety-blickety, right twarg de Hebrew chilluns. And in front of hit all was old King

Pharaoh hisself, drivin' a pair of bay hosses and swingin' his swowd and cussin' and hollerin' and goin' on mighty mean.

"Dar now," say Moses. "From de looks of yonder, y'all ain't got far to go, do you want old King Pharaoh to boss you. You don't has to go to Egypt, 'cause from de looks of what I see comin', Egypt is comin' to git you."

So all de Hebrew chilluns got skeered, and Moses went to de Lawd.

"What you reckon dat scound'el is up to, Lawd?" say Moses.

"Don't reckon nothin' 'bout hit," say de Lawd. "He's up to comin' out yar and slayin' de Hebrew chilluns. Dat's what he up to."

"You ain't gonter let him do hit, is you, Lawd?" say Moses.

"Hit's you and Pharaoh about dat, Moses," say de Lawd. "I been doin' de best I kin wid y'all, and de boys is grumblin' and growlin' and want to quit me for Pharaoh. And I ain't a man which is gonter go outer my way to help a man which don't want help."

"But, Lawd," say Moses, "you got us in dis mess, and we sho hopes you gonter git us out."

"Whyn't you outrun him?" say de Lawd.

"Can't run over de Red Sea," say Moses.

"Well," say de Lawd, "whyn't you dodge to de right or de left?"

"Can't," say Moses. "Hit's a canebrake on one side and a swamp on de yuther. We's jest natchally hemmed in. Dat's all."

"I yared some of de boys tawkin' bout goin' back to Egypt," say de Lawd. "Hit looks like now is a mighty good time to start back."

"And run smack into King Pharaoh's war chariots?" say Moses. "Lawd, dis ain't no time to play. Us is in a mess of trouble, Lawd."

"Trouble?" say de Lawd. "In trouble, did you say?"

"Yassuh," say Moses.

"I be doggone efn hit don't look like from whar I'm settin' dat y'all is smack in de dozens. Efn I ain't fooled, y'all is square betwixt de devil and de deep blue sea, only hit's Pharaoh and red instid of old Satan and blue. But hit's about de same thing."

"Lawd, hit ain't no time ——" Moses start to say. But de Lawd settle down in his cloud and start to singin':

"De blind man stood in de road and he cried.
De blind man stood in de road and he cried.

De blind man stood in de road and he cried,
Cryin', O Lawd, save-a me."

So Moses seed he wa'n't gonter git no more
tawk from de Lawd, so he went on back to
where de Hebrew chilluns was. De women was
moanin' and de men was groanin'.

"What did de Lawd tole you, Moses?" say de
Hebrew chilluns.

"Said he's hidin' behime a cloud and ain't
skeered," say Moses.

"What did he said about us?"

"Said us was betwixt de devil and de deep
blue," say Moses.

"He got hit figgered out about right, too,"
say de Hebrew men, "but dat ain't keepin' my
old lady from bein' a widow woman."

"De Lawd ack like he ain't intrusted no
more," say Moses. "He say y'all been wantin'
to go back to Egypt, so he made up his mind he
gonter let you go."

So they argyed and argyed, to finally ev'y-
body swore they ain't never said they wanted
to go to Egypt, and efn they did said hit, they
was jest tawkin'. And den one of de ladies re-
solved dat ev'ybody git in a circle and ax de
Lawd to help 'em. So they circled up and hol-

lered three times: "O Lawd, save us! O Lawd, save us! O Lawd, save us!"

So when they said dat, out stepped de Lawd.

"Dat tawk is mighty diffunt from de tawk y'all been makin'," say de Lawd.

"Dat yuther tawk was jest mouf tawk," say de Hebrew chilluns. "Dis tawk comes from de heart."

"Well," say de Lawd, "maybe hit do and maybe hit don't. But, anyways, I'm gonter do a little tawkin' myself, now. I got y'all jest whar I kin tawk sense to you and I'm gonter tawk some."

"Tawk, Lawd," say de Hebrew chilluns.

"Well," say de Lawd, "who is de Lawd round yar? Me or Pharaoh?"

"You, all de time, Lawd," say de Hebrew chilluns.

"Who brang y'all outn Egypt?"

"You, Lawd," say de Hebrew chilluns.

"Which is better, marchin' wid me or makin' bricks wid Pharaoh?"

"Marchin' wid you, Lawd," say de Hebrew chilluns.

"Well, who kin you count on when you's in trouble? Me or Pharaoh?"

[130]

"You, Lawd, all de time, Lawd."

"Well," say de Lawd, "jest don't forgit. Now, Moses, take yo' rod and make a pass at dat Red Sea." And Moses made a pass and de Red Sea runned uphill to hit was dry land.

"Now git on across," say de Lawd. And de Hebrew chilluns got.

So about de time they got across, yar come Pharaoh drivin' after 'em, but Moses waved his rod ag'in widout de Lawd tellin' him, and de sea swaged back and drownded Pharaoh and his army.

"Dat's right," say de Lawd. "You's gittin' handy wid dat rod, Moses."

"I don't know much, Lawd," say Moses, "but I'm learnin'. And I'm gonter start a revival meetin' right yar and now. Some of you womenfolks start de hym's whilst I finds me a text to preach about."

The Big Lodge

WELL, when de Hebrew chilluns got safe across de Red Sea and held a revival meetin', de Lawd started 'em marchin' again.

"Y'all ain't hardly started twarg de Promise' Land," de Lawd told Moses. "Ain't hardly got started yit."

"Marchin' all day, Lawd," say Moses, "sho does git tiresome. Hit's so stiddy."

"You got all night to rest up in, ain't you?" say de Lawd.

"Restin' gits tiresome, too," say Moses. "Jest marchin' and restin'."

"Well," say de Lawd, "I been sort of thinkin' 'bout organizin' a lodge to keep de folks occupied endurin' between supper and bedtime."

"Already got a lodge," say Moses.

"Yeah?" say de Lawd. "What kind of lodge?"

"Not much," say Moses. "Hit's mainly for de young folks to sing and dance. Aaron organized hit."

"I don't like dat dancin', much," say de Lawd. "I'm ag'in' hit."

"Hit ain't much lodge, Lawd," say Moses. "I didn't jine. They don't even got a goat to initiate de new members wid."

"Naw?" say de Lawd. "What do they initiate wid?"

"A calf," say Moses. "A yearlin' calf."

"Well, I be doggone," say de Lawd. "And chargin' dues, too, I bet."

"Course dey charges dues," say Moses.

"Well," say de Lawd, "I ain't aimin' to put up wid dat kind of lodge among my people. A calf! Well, I jest be dad blamed! Moses, you go right out yonder and tell Aaron to turn dat calf back in de pasture and break up dat lodge.

Do y'all want a lodge, well, I'll organize one my own se'f."

So Moses told Aaron what de Lawd say.

"Well," say Aaron, "hit ain't much lodge, but hit's better den no lodge. But I guess you and de Lawd ought to git out a purty good one."

"When I and de Lawd gits done organizin' our lodge," say Moses, "you kin jest bet yo' bottom dollar hit'll be a lodge, all right. A calf! Humph!"

So Aaron turned de calf loose and Moses went on over behind de cloud and told de Lawd.

"Moses," say de Lawd, "dis is gonter be a lodge which'll be bigger and better den any lodge in town. Hit's gonter be my lodge and I'm gonter be de High Supreme Potentate my ownse'f and all of my people is gonter be members."

"Lawd," say Moses, "how 'bout me bein' de Inner Gyard?"

"Be anything you want to, Moses," say de Lawd. "Potentate is my job 'cause hit's my lodge. De members kin have de yuther jobs. I don't keer who is what."

"What gonter be de password, Lawd?" say Moses.

"Ain't no password," say de Lawd. "But ev'ybody got to know de by-laws by heart."

"Dat's a funny kind of lodge, Lawd," say Moses. "What is de dues?"

"Obeyin' de by-laws is all de dues you got to pay," say de Lawd.

"How bout de goat to initiate de new members wid?" say Moses.

"De fust man which breaks de by-laws," say de Lawd, "I'm gonter make him wish he was a goat."

"Sounds mighty mysterious," say Moses. "What is de by-laws?"

"Set down and git yo' pencil and paper and write 'em down whilst I says 'em off to you," say de Lawd.

"I ain't got no paper," say Moses, "nor neither no pencil."

"Well, git a flat rock, den," say de Lawd, "and scratch 'em on hit wid yo' pocket knife."

So Moses got a flat rock and his knife, and de Lawd started sayin' off de by-laws.

"Lawd," say Moses, "dat sounds mighty like de Ten Commandments."

"Dat's zackly what hit is," say de Lawd. "Jest you scratch 'em down."

So Moses sot and scratched and de Lawd sot and talked out de Ten Commandments.

"Dat all?" say Moses.

"Hit's a heap," say de Lawd. "Jest you make ev'ybody learn 'em by heart and obey 'em. And efn you don't has yo' hands full you kin write me down as a sinner."

"And hit ain't no goat?" say Moses.

"De fust man which breaks 'em," say de Lawd, "is gonter wish he wa'n't nothin' but a goat. 'Cause I'm gonter march him to his tongue mighty nigh drags de ground. And den I ain't gonter let him enter de Promise' Land."

Well, de more Moses thought about de Lawd's idea for a lodge, de better he liked hit. "Oughter be easy to keep de folks out of devilment in dis lodge," he say. "And does ev'ybody stay out of devilment, maybe de Lawd won't march us so hard."

So Moses went on back to camp. But when he got there he got mad, 'cause old Aaron had done kotched dat calf again and had his caif lodge goin' strong. Aaron would take a new member and blindfold him and say, "Now bend over and kiss de Bible." And about de time de new member got bunt over good, de Inner Gyard would turn dat calf loose at him. And ker-blam! Hit's be a week before de new member could set down again!

"You, Aaron!" hollered Moses. "I thought I told you to stop dat fool calf lodge!"

"Yeah, you told me," say Aaron. "But vou ain't de Lawd round hyar."

"Well," say Moses, "I ain't de Lawd, but I'm de Lawd's wawkin' boss."

"I ain't studdin' who you is," say Aaron. "Dis is a good lodge and us is havin' a heap of fun. Now jest drag yo'se'f on out, or I'll have de Inner Gyard initiate you, jest like de rest of 'em."

"Adjourn dis lodge right now," say Moses, gittin' madder.

"Git him, Inner Gyard," say Aaron. And de Inner Gyard started twarg Moses.

"Stand back," say Moses, "or I'll knock somebody down." So de Inner Gyard stopped and looked at Aaron.

"Git him," say Aaron. And he started at Moses again.

So Moses up wid de rock which he'd writ de Ten Commandments on, and ker-blip! De Inner Gyard thought lightnin' had done struck him!

But dat wa'n't all. De Ten Commandment rock bounced offn de Inner Gyard and tuck de calf on de haid and kilt him, too, and den rolled on de floor and busted. And about dat time hit got dark and thundered and lightnined, and de yearth shuck. And when things cleared up, dar stood de Lawd.

"What's goin' on round hyar?" say de Lawd.

"Ain't nothin', Lawd," say Aaron. "Not nothin' else onless you says."

So de Lawd turned to Moses. "Whar's my Ten Commandments?" he says.

Moses p'inted to de floor.

"Well, I be doggone!" say de Lawd. "Done broke ev'y one of 'em in one bunch," he say. "I reckon dat's about de world's record."

"Hit was a accident," say Moses.

"Accident de dog's foot!" say de Lawd. "I seed you th'ow 'em at de Inner Gyard. Come yar tawkin' 'bout accidents to me! You jest drag yo'se'f right back up de mountain and write dem Ten Commandments down again, and git back yar and start dis lodge."

Moses done jest like de Lawd say, but he never lived to git to de Promise' Land, 'cause he busted de Lawd's Ten Commandments.

Crossing Jordan

WELL, hit was some mighty men among de Hebrew chilluns, but Moses was beyunt 'em all. For fawty years he led de Hebrews, rain or shine, up de hills and down de hollows, cross de deserts and through de waters. When he run into somethin' and de Lawd wa'n't handy, old Moses would jest r'ar back and raise his rod and pass a miracle on hit.

"I ain't braggin', Lawd," say Moses, "but I'm gittin' powerful handy wid dat rod. So any

[139]

time you want to rest up some, jest let me know and I'll take care of de chilluns."

"Moses," say de Lawd, "when I made you my wawkin' boss I app'inted you my head man, next to me. I gave you dat rod and you learned how to handle hit. When my chilluns grumbled, you preached to 'em. When they sinned, you prayed for 'em. Moses, all I got to say is you's a mighty good man. Mighty good. But you's a man, and you's made out of meat."

Well, Moses didn't know what de Lawd was drivin' at, but he wa'n't no man to ax questions from de Lawd, so he went on back to leadin' de Hebrew chilluns. But wawkin' along, he got a gimp in his laig.

"Wet j'ints," he say. "Must be fixin' to rain." But hit seem like de faster he'd try to wawk de shorter his steps got.

So hit was a young man marchin' right behind Moses, named Joshua.

"Moses," say Joshua, "whyn't you set down and rest and let me lead dis line around today? Course I know I can't do hit as good as you kin, but I been watchin' how you done hit, and I got a idea."

"All right, son," say Moses. "I got a gimp in

my laig and I don't seem to be makin' much time."

"I knowed hit was somethin' like dat," say Joshua. "Some of de boys say hit's because you's gittin' old. But I tells 'em, I say, 'Moses ain't gittin' old. He ain't hardly a hund'ed and twenty, yit.'"

So old Moses gimped along a few steps. "Joshua," he say, "you see dat little blue cloud over yonder?"

"Yassuh, Moses," say Joshua.

"Well," say Moses, "de Great I Am is ridin' in dat cloud. Jest keep yo' eye on hit and follow hit. Do somethin' git in yo' way or de boys git thirsty, jest holler for either me or de Lawd. I'm gonter wait to de wagons come up and pick me a ride."

So Joshua led de Hebrews and ev'ything was gittin' long fine. To all at once dey come out of de woods and right up to de bank of a deep, wide river.

"Hold on hyar," say Joshua, "whilst I looks about some." So he looked about, but he couldn't find no place he could wade de river. So he say, "F'm de looks of how deep dat river

[141]

is, I better call Moses and de Lawd too." And
he called 'em bofe.

"When hit ain't nothin' but jest plain
marchin', Moses," Joshua say, "I ain't a man
which'll holler for help. But when hit comes
to crossin' rivers, I'm de fust man to squall."

"Dat's right, Joshua," say Moses. "Only you
hadn't ought to disturb de Lawd on a little old
river like dis. I'm a plenty." So he wawked up
to de water and laid down his rod and say,
"River, run uphill so de Lawd's chilluns kin
wawk across." And he stepped back and waited.

But de river jest kept on runnin' downhill.

So Moses lifted up his rod and smit de river
seven times and told hit again, but de river jest
kept on runnin'. He tried hit again and again,
to he had tried hit seven times, but he didn't
have no luck. And den he looked at de Lawd.

"Lawd," he say, "I know what you was drivin'
at de yuther day when you said I was made out
of meat. I know dis gimp in my laig ain't wet
j'ints, too, Lawd. Hit's old age creepin' on me.
So, Lawd, you better take dis rod and dry up de
river for yo' chilluns. I done about done my
do."

De Lawd jest sot there, rockin' back and forth,

[142]

lookin' 'way 'cross de river at somethin' for a long time. Den he looked at Moses and den he looked 'cross de river again.

"Moses," he say, finally, "le's ev'ybody set down and tawk dis thing out, right yar and now." So ev'ybody sot.

"Dis river," say de Lawd, "is de Jurdin. And hit's de last river a man got to cross before he gits to de Promise' Land. I named hit de Promise' Land 'cause I promise' old Abraham I'm gonter let his grandchilluns farm dat land, 'way back yonder before any of y'all boys was born.

"Well, I'm gonter take y'all 'cross dis river to de Promise' Land, 'cause when I promise somebody somethin', I means what I says."

"Amen, Lawd," say Moses.

"But," say de Lawd, "you got to learn to take yo' time. I marched y'all up and down de wilderness fawty years, rain or shine, jest to show you how to take yo' time. And maybe I ain't as smart as some of y'all Hebrew boys, and I knows I ain't as smart as some of y'all think you is. But I been wawkin' up and down de yearth a mighty long time, and I ain't been wawkin' wid my years stopped up and my eyes shut. I knows a

couple of things. And one of 'em is, you got to
learn how to take yo' time."

"Amen, Lawd," say Moses.

"Right 'cross dat river," say de Lawd, "is de
land flowin' wid milk and honey. Milk is good
to drink, and honey is good to eat."

"Amen, Lawd, amen," say de Hebrew chilluns.

"But s'posin'," say de Lawd, "a man ain't
never had nothin' to drink but milk, and nothin'
to eat but honey? He'd git mighty sick and
tired of milk and honey and go to beggin' for
cabbages and cawn bread. Dat's jest how come
de Projeckin' Son went out and et cawn wid de
hawgs. He'd been eatin' nothin' but fat barbecue calf for so long to he got so he jest couldn't
look a calf in de face and hold his stomach down.
Old King Nebuchadnezzar had so much good
licker and so much good vittles and so many
purty women round him all de time to finally he
jest got up and went out in de pasture and ate
grass like a mule. All because he didn't know
how to take his time.

"Verily I say unto you, blessed are de pace-
makers which wawks slow behind me, 'cause
they know how to take they time."

"Amen," say Moses.

"I marched y'all fawty years," say de Lawd,
"and endurin' dat time you ain't been doin'
much heavy eatin' and drinkin'. I ain't made yo'
bellies so happy, but I sho whetted up yo' appetites so's you kin enjoy de vittles on de yuther
side of Jurdin."

"Praise de Lawd," say de Hebrew chilluns.

"Now when I swages de waters back so y'all
kin cross," say de Lawd, "is y'all gonter run
'cross like a bunch of hawgs after cawn, or is
y'all gonter march across like you had some man-
ners and raisin'?"

"March 'cross, Lawd," say Moses. "We gonter take our time and march."

De Lawd looked at Moses. "Moses," he say,
"dat's wrong. They gonter march, maybe, but
not you."

"How come, Lawd?" say Moses. "Ain't I de
wawkin' boss?"

"Not no more, Moses," say de Lawd.

So Moses sot and studied and studied. "Well,
Lawd," he say, "when you promise me somethin'
good you always give hit to me. And when you
promise me somethin' bad, I ain't a man to kick
about gittin' hit, too. I ain't forgot about
busten all dem Ten Commandments on de calf's

[145]

haid, back yonder. You promise' efn I busted
'em I couldn't git to de Promise' Land. And I
busted ev'y one of 'em, Lawd. I ain't complainin'."

"Moses," say de Lawd, "I ain't holdin' dat
ag'in' you. I ain't holdin' nothin' ag'in' you.
And efn I could, I'd let you lead de Hebrew chilluns 'cross Jurdin. But I can't. Hit's a mighty
mystery de way I got to run my yearth, and
sometimes hit look like I'm bein' hard on my best
people. But I ain't. Hit's jest part of de
mystery."

"You's right, ev'y time, Lawd," say Moses.

"I ain't braggin', but I ain't never been wrong
yit," say de Lawd. "So, Moses, hit's jest like you
say. You's gittin' along in de years. You done
done yo' do, and yo' time is out. Joshua is a
young man and a good man. He ain't got as
much sense as you, but he's got a heap more
strenk. And I needs a leader wid a heap of
strenk. So I'm makin' him my head man."

"Joshua ain't nobody's fool, too, Lawd," say
Moses. "He's got a heap of sense."

So ev'ybody jest sot, rockin' back and forth,
lookin' 'cross de river. To finally Moses say:
"Lawd, efn hit's all de same to you, I'll jest set

and watch de Hebrew chilluns march past, and den I and de old lady will settle down and plant a little gyarden whare us kin set and look over Jurdin, even efn us can't cross."

So Moses sot, but about dat time somethin' caught him up and before he could bat his eye he was settin' in middle of de air, and a cherub was lacin' golden slippers on his tired feet, and angels was puttin' a white robe on his tired shoulders, and de Lawd was puttin' a golden crown on his tired haid.

"Lawd," say Moses, "dis is mighty nice. Mighty nice. Thanky, Lawd."

"Moses," say de Lawd, "dis ain't de Promise' Land I promised Abraham's grandchildren, but hit's de Promise' Land for all good folks."

"Well, hit's mighty nice, Lawd," say Moses.

The Stratagem of Joshua

WHEN de Lawd swaged de Jurdin so de Hebrew chilluns could cross, Joshua lined 'em up and de Lawd stepped out f'm behind his cloud and made a speech.

"Chillun," he say, "I been leadin' y'all fawty years f'm Egypt to the Promise' Land. Now yar is y'all, and yar is de Promise' Land. I promise' old Abraham I'd bring y'all yar, and so yar you is."

"Looks mighty good," say Joshua.

"Hit is good," say de Lawd, "and all y'all got

to do is farm hit. So I'm gonter turn hit over
to you yar and now, and I'm goin' on back and
'tend to my angels awhile. Joshua is my haid
man and he kin go to de cou't-house and git de
papers fixed up. But de p'int is, I promise' y'all
dis land and yar hit is and yar you is. So take
keer of yo'se'f and don't git in no trouble."

So de Lawd stepped back in his cloud and rid
off, and about dat time yar come a gal, wawkin'
down de road, sellin' fish and singin':

> "Better buy my fish, I got a little bit left—
> Better buy my fish, I got a little bit left—
> Better buy my fish, I got a little bit left—
> Efn you don't buy 'em, gonter eat 'em myse'f."

So she wawked up to Joshua. "Hy-dy, Big
Boy!" she say. "Don't you want to buy some
fish?"

"I ain't lame," say Joshua. "Do I wants some
fish, I kin go fishin'."

"You's hard, ain't you, Country Boy," say de
gal. "Come yar givin' a lady like me dat kind
of sass. Better mind out. I'll git my man to
come out yar and he'll beat you ha'f to death."

"Yo' man and who else?" say Joshua.

"Listen at dat man tawk!" say de gal. "You
sho tawks mean, don't you? Me, I'm a nice

[149]

gal, and you ain't did a thing but shawt-tawk me ev'y since I wawked up. Cou'se I ain't so purty, like some gals, but I's a nice lady."

"You ain't so hard to look at, lady," say Joshua. "What's yo' name?"

"Rahab," say de gal. "What's yo'n?"

"Dat's a purty name, Miss Rahab," say Joshua. "My name is Joshua. And de reason I tawked so hard at you is 'cause I's de Lawd's haid man over de Hebrew chilluns and I got to ack hard. I can't he'p hit."

"Who de Lawd?" say Rahab. "And who de Hebrew chilluns?"

"Who de Lawd, did you say?" say Joshua. "My goodness! gal, ain't you never yared tell of de Lawd? Whar was you brang up at?"

"Nawp," say Rahab, "I ain't never yared tell of de Lawd, nor neither de Hebrew chilluns."

"Well," say Joshua, "de Lawd ain't only de man which owns all de yearth, but he's de man which made de yearth. And heaven, too. And mighty nigh ev'ything else you kin think about."

"Sounds big, don't hit," say Rahab. "Who de Hebrew chilluns?"

"They's de chillun which de Lawd gived all disyar land to 'em," say Joshua.

"Dat's funny," say Rahab. "De Philistines over yonder at Jericho ain't yared de news about de Hebrew chilluns ownin' dis land. They's tellin' hit about dat they owns de land they-se'f."

"They gonter yar de news mighty soon," say Joshua. " 'Cause next to de Lawd, I'm de head man, and I'm gonter tell 'em de news. And when I spreads news, hit's 'most gen'ally sad news."

"I bet hit is, you good-lookin' scound'el," say Rahab. "But de only thing is, de fo'ks at Jericho got a wall round de town and quick as somebody come yar to make trouble dey gits inside and shet de gate. And de fust somebody which pokes his haid over de wall gits hit busted wid a rock."

"I ain't skeered of de Philistines," say Joshua.

"Listen at me, man," say Rahab. "You might ain't skeered of de Philistines. But jest as sho as you stick yo' haid over dat wall, one of 'em is gonter hit you wid a rock and you ain't gonter know is hit now or next week. Now jest listen at me and I'm gonter tell you some news."

"Tell hit, sister," say Joshua.

"Well," say Rahab, "f'm de looks of things, y'all looks like you kin march right good."

"Us had a heap of practice de last fawty years," say Joshua. "We ain't been doin nothin' else but marchin'."

"But you ain't been doin' no wall-climbin' and no fightin'?"

"Nawp," say Joshua, "us ain't."

"Well," say Rahab, "whyn't you jest march dat city down?"

"Gal," say Joshua, "I'm a fightin' man, and dat ain't no way to fight. How you gonter march a city down, anyhow?"

"Do jest like I tell you," say Rahab. "You line up yo' men and give 'em a ram hawn and a swowd. And ev'y mawnin', at de crack of day, march up mighty nigh to de walls like you comin' right over, but jest before you gits dar, turn and march round de town, and den go back to camp and stay in camp to de next mawnin'. Do jest like dat for six days, and on de seventh day start out de same way, only don't go back to camp, but jest keep on marchin' round de city."

"Ain't no sense in dat," say Joshua.

"And hit won't be no sense in yo' haid do a Philistine bust you wid a rock, too," say Rahab.

[152]

"Well," say Joshua, "anything to please de womenfolks."

Rahab grins. "I knowed you was a smart man," she say. "Now do jest like I tells you, but don't let on to nobody I told you. You jest march, and efn ev'ything goes all O.K. I'll make a sign at you f'm my window."

So de next mawnin' Joshua lined up his army and passed out de ram hawns and de swowds and marched round de town, blowin' and carryin' on to you jest oughter yar de noise! So 'bout de time he got round he seed somebody wavin' de handkercher out de window and he looked, and sho nuff hit was Rahab.

"See you tomorrow mawnin', Good-lookin'," he hollered.

"Same back at you, Big Boy," she say.

So de next day de same thing happen. And de next. To finally they'd marched six days. So on de seventh day Joshua marched round jest like he been, but instid of goin' back to camp, he jest kept right on marchin', round and round. To he marched round seven times. Den de yearth moaned and groaned and de walls shivered and shuck, and ker-blam! they fell down.

When de walls tumbled, de Hebrew army

[153]

th'owed down de ram hawns and got they swowds and waded in on dat sinful city. Some folks say they sp'iled hit. But de ones which was present and seen what happened say they jest natchally ruint hit.

"Well, I be doggone," say Joshua. "Dat's quar. Dem walls went down jest like hit was dinny-mite under 'em. And I didn't yar no dinny-mite bust." So 'bout dat time he looked up and yar come Rahab.

"Hello, Big Boy!" she say.

"Hello, Sweetenin'!" say Joshua. "Tell me somethin'. How come deseyar walls fall down when I didn't yar no dinny-mite bust?"

Rahab th'owed back her haid and laughed. "Hit's a heap of things you don't know," she say, "and did I tell you what I know, den you'd know as much as me."

"Aw, come on, gal," say Joshua. "Tell me."

"Well," say Rahab, "hit might of been like dis. Onderstand? I say hit might. Hit might of been dat all de boys in de city seed y'all comin' de fust day, and got ready for a fight. But naw. Y'all didn't come to fight. Y'all jest marched around and went on home. So dat looked like a trick and hit onsettled 'em. So de

[154]

next day de same thing happened, and dat worried 'em some mo'. And hit kept on to finally they was expectin' ev'ything and gittin' nothin'. So on de last day, when you marched round seven times, hit was jest mo'n they could stand. So they jest pushed down de walls f'm de inside."

"Yeah," say Joshua, "dat's jest about de way I had hit figgered out, all de time."

"Yeah, you did," say Rahab. Den her voice got deep, like a man's. "Yeah you did—not."

So Joshua looked at her, and while he was lookin' she faded out and dar stood de Lawd. "Yeah, you had hit figgered out like dat, Joshua," say de Lawd. "Now listen at me and let me tell you somethin'."

So Joshua listened.

"I pushed dem walls down," say de Lawd, "jest like I pushed back de Red Sea and de Jurdin."

"But, Lawd," say Joshua, "I was standin' yar, tawkin' to a lady friend, and I looks and she's gone and yar you stands."

De Lawd kind of laughed. "Yeah," he say. "Dat woman you was tawkin' to wa'n't nobody but me. I comed to you by a woman, dat's all. Hit's one of my tricks."

"But how come, Lawd?" say Joshua.

"Well," say de Lawd, "efn you had been old man Moses, I'd jest 'a' wawked up to you and told you to march round dis town seven times, to de walls fell, and Moses'd 'a' marched, rain or shine. But you's a young man, Joshua, and I had to trick you. Efn I had told you to march, you'd 'a' marched about twice, and de fust good-lookin' gal come along, you'd a stopped marchin' and gone to courtin' her. So I comed to you like a woman and made you court me all de time you was doin' my commands."

So Joshua laughed. "Lawd," he say, "dat was a good trick on me. And you sho was a good-lookin' woman, too!"

"Yeah," say de Lawd, "but no mind dat. You jest watch out, 'cause de next dress you start runnin' after is liable to be on a sho-nuff woman, and den whar'd you be?"

The Sun Trick

WHEN Joshua seed how easy hit was to trick de enemies at Jericho, he went trickin' all de towns about. He'd take and split his army in two and make half of 'em hide in de bushes and de yuther half follow him. Den he'd march up in front of a town and start beggin' for a fight.

"I'm a fighter from Fightersville and I craves

[157]

action," he'd say. "Efn y'all is skeered to fight me, jest say so and I'll fight myse'f. Jest march yo' measly army out yar and I'll run 'em to they tongues drag de ground."

So de town would march de army out and old Joshua would start backin' up. And de town army would come at 'em and Joshua would light out. Den, 'bout de time de town army was chasin' Joshua, de yuther army which was hidin' in de bushes would git up and set de town on fire and den git at de town's army from behind. And den old Joshua would swarm all over dat town army like flies at de molasses bar'l.

"Joshua," say de Lawd, "you'se a good trick fighter, but I'm gonter see how you is on jest plain, natchal fightin'."

"Well, Lawd," say Joshua, "I ain't braggin', but I claims to be a natchal fighter fust and a trick fighter next. Who round yar is lookin' for a natchal fight wid me?"

"Well," say de Lawd, "hit's a king name King Adonizec which is powerful intrusted in a fight."

"I kin lick him wid my eyes shet," say Joshua.

"And hit's a king name King Homan, too," say de Lawd.

"Humph!" say Joshua. "He ain't so much."

"And old King Piram was down to de store de yuther day wid a chip on his shoulder," say de Lawd.

"He's my meat," say Joshua.

"And I yared tell dat King Japhi was hankerin' for trouble."

"Let him look at me," say Joshua.

"And," say de Lawd, "hit's a king name King Bebir which passed de word round dat he's jest champin' at de bit for a fight."

"Bebir ain't hardly nothin'," say Joshua. "I kin take 'em all on, one at de time, and whup de whole pa'cel of 'em before breakfus."

"One at de time, yeah," say de Lawd. "But from de news I yars, you ain't gonter git a whack at 'em one at de time."

"Lawd, you don't mean dem boys is gonter gang up on me?" say Joshua.

"Dat's jest zackly what dey done did," say de Lawd.

"Well, great day in de mawnin'!" say Joshua. "What do you think about dat, Lawd?"

"Looks like hit's gonter be a natchal fight," say de Lawd.

[159]

"Natchal fight is right," say Joshua. "You gonter stick by me, ain't you, Lawd?"

"I ain't never runned away from a fight yit, when my people was fightin'," say de Lawd. "And I'm too old to start runnin' now."

So old Joshua lined up his army at de crack of day and he marched out and pitched in at dem five kings. And you better believe Joshua and dem kings fit. Up de hills and down de hollows. They jest natchally fit all over de Promise' Land. Fust one side was ahead and den de yuther, but they jest kept right on fightin'.

"We ain't gittin' nowheres wid dis fight, Lawd," say Joshua. "Fust hit's me ahead, and den hit's de five kings. Hit looks like to me dis fight is liable to end in a tie efn somethin' don't happen."

"Hit sho is some fight," say de Lawd.

"Yeah," say Joshua. "I been tryin' to trick 'em some, but dem boys don't trick worth a durn. They jest fights."

"What kind of trick you been tryin', Joshua?" say de Lawd.

"Well, I tried dat marchin' trick like us worked at Jericho," say Joshua, "but dem boys knows as much about dat trick as me and you

does. Den I tried to hide my army in de bushes.
But dem scound'els had a army hidin' in de
bushes, too. So I tried to march like I'm gonter
come at 'em from de front and swing round and
hit 'em in de flanks."

"Dat didn't work?" say de Lawd.

"Work?" say Joshua. "I say she didn't. Dem
scound'els flanked right back at me. I never
seed such fighters."

"Hit sho is some fight," say de Lawd. "Win,
lose, or tie, hit's some fight."

"I wish I had me a rod like Moses had," say
Joshua.

"How come?" say de Lawd.

"I would try a new trick on 'em which I can't
try onless I got a Moses rod," say Joshua.

"What trick is dat?" say de Lawd.

"Hit's a sun trick," say Joshua. "I'd wait to
de sun gits about a hour high, and I'd work
hit."

"I wouldn't wait to de sun gits dat low," say
de Lawd. "Hit wouldn't be long to dark, and
efn you can't whup dese boys in de light, how
you gonter whup 'em in de dark?"

"Dat's part of de trick," say Joshua.

"Well," say de Lawd, "I ain't gonter give you

no Moses rod. But I'll give you power to pass one miracle, efn dat'll do any good."

"One is enough," say Joshua. "Now you kin go on and set behind yo' cloud, 'cause I got dem boys as good as licked right now."

"Well," say de Lawd, "they don't look like they's licked to me."

"Jest go on to yo' cloud, Lawd," say Joshua. "Leave dem boys to me."

"All right, Joshua," say de Lawd. "But all de same, I b'lieve I'm gonter tote a few rocks over wid me and when I see a enemy standin' under my cloud, I'm gonter drap a rock on his haid."

"Suit yo'se'f, Lawd," say Joshua. "But don't drap no rock on my men, 'cause, from de looks of things, I need ev'y man I got."

So de Lawd went to his cloud and Joshua and de kings fit and fit. Fust one side was ahead and den de yuther. And ev'y now and den de Lawd would ketch a enemy standin' under his cloud, and he'd kind of turn his haid and ease a rock down on him and say, "Enemies, count yo' soldiers," and he'd settle back to another got under. And he didn't miss a man. But hit was so many enemies to they jest kept on fightin'.

To finally Joshua looked up and seed de sun was about a hour high.

"Now I'm gonter pass my miracle," he say. So he r'ared way back and hollered three times, "Sun, stand still! Sun, stand still! Sun, stand still!" So de sun stood still and Joshua kept right on fightin'.

So de Lawd stepped out and told Joshua, "Joshua, I don't see no need in makin' de sun stand still. You ain't no better off den you was when de fight started. I'm gonter git me some mo' rocks."

"Jest watch me," say Joshua, and he started circlin' round. Den all at once he r'ared back and give de command to his army: "Army," he say, "go git 'em." And his army waded in.

Well, from dat time on de fight was as good as over. De kings kept backin' up, waitin' for de sun to set, but de sun didn't set. And Joshua kept right behind 'em. To finally de kings backed in a cave and Joshua rolled a stone over de mouf. And dat put a end to de five kings which fit wid Joshua.

"Joshua," say de Lawd, "dat was a good fight, and I want to be de fust man to say so. But

what I want to know is, what did de sun had to
do wid hit."

"Ev'ything," say Joshua. "When de sun gits
about a hour high, hit shines right square in a
man's eye and blinds him. But jest for a minute,
'cause when de sun gits dat low, hit sinks purty
fast. But I waited to hit got jest right and I
made hit stand still. Den I worked round and
put my back to de sun and had hit shinin' right
in de enemies' eyes. And den I sailed in and
whupped 'em."

"Well, I be doggone," say de Lawd. "I yared
of a natchal-bawn fighter and I yared of a trick
fighter. But you is de fust man I ever seed
which was a natchal-bawn fighter and a trick
fighter, too. You's jest all right, Joshua."

"You ain't such a bad shot wid dem rocks
yo'se'f, Lawd," say Joshua. "I seed you droppin'
dem rocks, and I ain't never seed you had to drap
mo' den one to change a enemy's mind."

"Yeah," say de Lawd, "I had a heap of practice wid drapin' things and strikin' folks down.
Forked lightnin' or a rock, hit ain't much dif-
funce."

"Well," say Joshua, "I had a little practice
trickin', too. I been doin' tricks all my life."

The Younger Generation

JOSHUA was a mighty man and a mighty fighter. But he was a man, jest like de rest of 'em. So

[165]

when he got along about a hund'ed and ten years old, he sont for de Lawd.

"Lawd," he say, "I'm gittin' 'long in de years. My eyes ain't like they uster be and I'm sort of fallin' off on my eatin', too. I specks my time is about up. So hit's a favor I wants to ax you, Lawd."

"Ax hit," say de Lawd, "and I'll see what I kin do for you."

"Well," say Joshua, "hyar us is in de Promise' Land. You gived hit to us, jest like you said. And hit's ourn by rights, ain't hit?"

"It is," say de Lawd. "Hit's yo'n by rights."

"Well," say Joshua, "de boys which been livin' yar is doin' a heap of argyin' and fightin' about hit."

"You been gittin' along mighty good wid de fightin', ain't you?" say de Lawd.

"Been gittin', Lawd," say Joshua. "And dat's jest de p'int. You see, I ain't as spry as I uster was, and I can't lead my armies like I uster could. You got to lead a army, Lawd, do you want to whup somebody. You can't jest set back and tell hit how to fight. You got to git up and show hit how to fight."

"I ain't 'sputin' dat," say de Lawd.

"Well," say Joshua, "you see how hit is. I can't lead my army, and de land is ourn by rights, so why don't you go on and pass a miracle and drive de enemies away widout no mo' fightin'?"

"Joshua," say de Lawd, "hit's jest two reasons which I ain't gonter drive de enemies out by a miracle. De fust one is, I don't want to. And de next one is, I ain't goin' to."

"How come, Lawd?" say Joshua.

"Well," say de Lawd, "hit wan't never yit a man which died which I didn't have another man to step in his place. Now I ain't low-ratin' you, Joshua, 'cause you been a mighty good man. And I ain't blamin' you for gittin' de idea ain't nobody kin do de job good as you been. Ev'ybody figures like dat when they gits old. But when you dies, de Hebrew chilluns is gonter git along."

"Dat's right, Lawd," say Joshua. "But I don't see how come a man got to fight for somethin' which is already hisn."

"Is de Promise' Land worth fightin' for, Joshua?" say de Lawd.

"Cou'se hit's worth fightin' for," say Joshua. "But ——"

"Don't but me," say de Lawd, " 'cause I know what I'm doin'. I'm makin' de Hebrew chilluns fight for dis land, 'cause do I jest give hit to 'em widout no trouble, they wouldn't want hit. Give a man somethin' and quick as he turns his back, he'll th'ow hit away. But sell him somethin' at a high price, and he'll hang on to de cows come home."

"I guess dat's right," say Joshua, "but all de same I done some mighty hard fightin' already. Dis is mighty good land, but I's fit mighty hard, Lawd."

"Dat's de p'int," say de Lawd. "You fit so hard to de yuther Hebrew boys didn't had to do so much fightin'. They got de land too easy on account of how hard you fit. So I'm gonter prophet to you. Did you keep on livin' you'd hang on to dis land to de cows come home. But quick as you die some of de young folks is gonter up and say, 'Easy come, easy go.' And they gonter git into trouble, 'cause they'll figure de rest will come as easy as dis."

"Well, Lawd," say Joshua, "they's yo chilluns and efn you wants to put 'em in trouble, hit's you and dem. But I fight mighty hard and I kind of hates to think about 'em gittin' in trouble."

"Well," say de Lawd, "I stuck by you, didn't I?"

"You did," say Joshua.

"And I stuck by Moses before you, too," say de Lawd. "I was stickin' by de Hebrew chilluns long before you was bawn, and I'm gonter be stickin' by 'em long after you's daid and gone. Sometime hit look like I done turned my back on 'em, and sometime hit look like I quit and gone on about my business. But I ain't. Hit's jest de way I do things. When hit looks like I'm ag'in' 'em de hardest, well, dat's about de time I pullin' for 'em de hardest. Hit's de way I got to run de yearth. I know hit's a mighty mystery to you, Joshua, but hit's plain as day to me. Hit's jest de way I does things."

So old Joshua hauled off and died and things turned up jest like de Lawd propheted. De young folks quit goin' to church and got to drinkin' and gamblin' and runnin' round at night, dancin' and good-timin' and carryin' on mighty nigh ev'y night. So when they'd line up to fight next day they wanted to sleep mo'n they did to fight. And de enemies lit in and licked

[169]

'em so quick they didn't know what minute was de next.

And when de enemies licked 'em, Lawd! Lawd! how they put de Hebrew chilluns to work! Chain-ganged ev'y lastin' one of 'em and worked 'em on de road from sun to sun.

And all de time de Lawd was settin' over behind his cloud and not sayin' a word. "They got a heap to learn," he say.

So de people worked and de Lawd watched. To finally de work got harder and de grub got worser. And when de enemies started monkeyin' wid they vittles, they sot dem Hebrew chilluns to thinkin'.

"Seem to me like," say a boy name Ehud, "dat my daddy uster tell me dis Promise' Land had milk and honey in hit."

"Yeah," say Judah, "dat was uster. But now hit ain't nothin' but work and trouble."

"Well," say Ehud, "I'm gittin' tired of eatin' cawn bread and cabbage. I'm goin' out and see can't I tawk to de Lawd about de way things is goin'." So he went out and bowed down. "Hyar me, Lawd, hyar me." But de Lawd didn't said a word. So Ehud hollered louder and louder. To finally de Lawd stuck his haid out from behind de cloud.

"You tawkin' to me?" he say.

"Lawd, I'm tryin' mighty hard to," say Ehud.

"I must of been sleepin'," say de Lawd. "Y'all ain't had nothin' to say to me in so long, I must of sot yar and dozed off. What you want to tawk to me about, Ehud?"

"A heap of things," say Ehud, and he told de Lawd how things was goin' on among de Hebrew chilluns.

"And you wants some help?" say de Lawd.

"Please, Lawd," say Ehud.

"Well," say de Lawd, "I'm purty busy. But hit ain't never yit nobody axed me for help and got turned down. Who been workin' y'all so hard on such short rations?"

"Old King Eglon," say Ehud.

"Dat lazy, fat scound'el?" say de Lawd. "Whyn't you up and kill him?"

"He's de king, Lawd," say Ehud.

"He ain't none of my king," say de Lawd.

"But how kin I kill him, Lawd?" say Ehud.

"You's left-handed, ain't you?" say de Lawd.

"Yassuh."

"Well, den," say de Lawd. "I ain't never yit

seed a left-handed man which couldn't trick a right-handed man wid a knife. Now you git you a butcher knife in yo' left hand, a rock in yo' right hand and go 'tend to dat lazy scound'el."

So Ehud got de rock and de knife, jest like de Lawd said, and he went before de king.

"Old King Eglun, live forever," say Ehud.

"I didn't send for you, Country Boy," say old King Eglun.

"I know you didn't, Yo' Majesty," say Ehud, " 'cause you got too much sense to send for trouble."

"What do you mean, Nothin'?" say old King Eglun.

"I mean," say Ehud, "dat trouble done come to you widout no invite."

"Humph!" say King Eglun. "Ain't nobody skeered of dat rock you got. I see dat rock in yo' hand quick as you wawked in de door."

"Well," say Ehud, "you's fixin' to feel hit now." So he got up and swung dat rock round his haid like he's gonter fling hit at de king, and de king dodged. And right dar was where he made his last mistake. 'Cause when he dodged de rock in Ehud's right hand, old Ehud tuck and stuck him wid de knife he was totin' in his left hand.

"Blessed be de name of de Lawd," say Ehud, " 'cause he learnt me how to lick his enemies." And from dat very day de news got scattered round about what had happened, and de enemies tuck and lit out and left de Hebrew chilluns alone for a while.

Battling With Baal

WELL, de Hebrew chilluns was de Lawd's chilluns, but they was jest chilluns. And chilluns ain't steady, I don't keer whose chilluns they is. So no quicker do old Ehud git 'em outn trouble and they settle down to they's up in trouble and devilment again. And quick as de Lawd caught 'em in devilment he sont de enemies after 'em. And when de enemies got 'em, you better believe hit was hard times among de Hebrew chilluns.

"Somethin' mighty funny 'bout dis," say de Hebrew chilluns. "Yar us is, claimin' we got de

Lawd on our side, and yar de enemies claimin' they got Baal on they side. And us is in de chain-gang and de enemies is in de clover. Maybe old Baal is got more stuff den de Lawd." So they quit prayin' to de Lawd and started prayin' to Baal.

So when de Lawd yared de news he got powerful mad, and he sont for a man named Gideon.

"Gideon," say de Lawd, "what's goin' on down yonder 'mongst my people?"

"Lawd," say Gideon, "ain't nothin' but trouble goin' on. I preached to yo' people ev'y Sunday, and I prays for 'em ev'y night. And they come right back and say, 'Well, efn de Lawd give us some action, we'll say our prayers to him, and efn he don't, well, we'll say our prayers to Baal!' "

"Dat what they sayin'?" say de Lawd.

"And doin'," say Gideon. "Lawd, you oughter git after dem sinful scound'els wid another flood. Or maybe take some broomstone to 'em."

"I ain't blamin' my chilluns," say de Lawd. "De chilluns is young and ain't got no better sense. But I'm gittin' mighty tired of old Baal messin' round. I yar he's holdin' a revival meetin' right in town."

"Been revivalin' all summer. Got his own church and ev'ything."

"Well, you go burn his church down, Gideon," say de Lawd.

So Gideon went and not only burnt Baal's church down, but he up and made a barbecue for de Lawd's people right in de ashes. And dat made old Baal mad.

"Who done dat?" he say.

"Me," say Gideon.

So old Baal backed up and cussed some, and den he called his members and say, "Members, dis boy done burnt my church down. What you gonter do about hit?"

"Whyn't you do somethin' 'bout hit, Baal?" say Gideon. "Hit was jest yo' church, and hit was jest me which burnt hit. From de way things looks hit ought to be jest me and you about hit."

"I ain't no fightin' man," say Baal, "but I got a heap of members which is jest achin' for a chance to fight."

"Well," say Gideon, "I ain't no fightin' man, too. Nor neither is de Lawd. But de Lawd told me to burn dat church down, and he 'lowed he

[176]

had a few members left which ain't never run from a fight yit."

So old Baal lined up all his members and Gideon lined up all de Lawd's members so's they could fight. And for ev'y member which was on de Lawd's side, hit was about ten members on Baal's side.

"I'm gonter make hamburgers outer yo' measly army," say Baal.

"Soap and water," say Gideon.

So 'bout dat time up wawked de Lawd. "Wait a minute," he say. "I got too many men on my side."

"But, Lawd," say Gideon, "we ain't got nigh as many as Baal's got."

"I got too many men," say de Lawd. "I don't never want nobody to say I ain't givin' Baal a fair fight, and dat's jest what they'd say, did I sail in at him wid all dese men. Send some of 'em home."

So Gideon told all de boys which ain't done plowin' de cotton crop to drap out and go home, and about half of his men went home.

"Now, dat looks better," say de Lawd.

"But, Lawd," say Gideon, "looky yonder at

[177]

old Baal. He got men swarmin' round him so thick they's jest workin'."

"You skeered?" say de Lawd.

"Nawsuh," say Gideon. "But some of my men is kind of skeered."

"Well," say de Lawd, "let all de men which is kind of skeered drap out and go home." So about half of what was left went home.

"Now de fight is gonter be about even, maybe," say de Lawd. "I sho don't want nobody to say I ganged up on Baal."

"Nobody never gonter say dat, Lawd," say Gideon. "Baal's men is as thick as flies round a molasses bar'l."

"Well, I sho hope they don't say I ganged on him," say de Lawd, "I might got too many men yit. Jest march 'em down to de creek for a drink of water and let me watch 'em drink."

So Gideon marched 'em down and some of 'em drap on they knees and drunk, and some of 'em tuck and dipped water up in they hats and drunk.

"Let ev'y man which knelt down and drunk drap out," say de Lawd. "I don't like to see a man on his knees a-drinkin'. I likes to see a man on his knees a-prayin' but not drinkin'." So de

[178]

mens which got on they knees and drunk went home, and dat left old Gideon three hund'ed men.

"Now, dis looks somethin' like," say de Lawd. "De fightin' is gittin' more even. Old Baal ain't got but about a million men on his side and us got three hund'ed. Dat's about right. But us still is got de under holts on him, and I can't stand to go at a man wid de under holts. Let ev'y man pile up his swowd in a pile."

"You know yo' business, Lawd," say Gideon, "but I be doggone efn I does. Baal got a million men wid swowds and us got only three hund'ed wid nothin' but they bare hands. Hit looks quar to me."

So 'bout dat time old Baal holler up, "We's champin' at de bits, waitin' for dat fight. We's jest achin' for trouble."

"Take yo' time, Baal," say de Lawd. "You gonter git all de trouble you kin handle as quick as I gits my army trimmed down to whar I kin handle hit."

So de Lawd puttered round mighty nigh all day, gittin' his men fixed fust one way and den de yuther, and 'lowin' he's awful skeered somebody gonter say he tuck advantage of Baal. So about sundown de Lawd say, "Dis jest won't do,

Gideon. Ev'y man I got is got two mighty good hands. S'posin' somebody found dat out? De fust thing you'd yar was somebody sayin' I tuck advantage of Baal. Now jest to settle dat argyment right yar before she gits started, let ev'y man tie his right hand behind him." So ev'y man tied.

"Now," say de Lawd, "de fight is gonter be about even. Gideon, you pass out a ram hawn to ev'y one of my men."

"Y'all better come on," hollered Baal. "Hit's gittin' dark."

"Take yo' time, Baal," say de Lawd. "Us will be along when us gits ready, and when us starts, you'll be de fust man to yar de news."

So de Lawd putters round some mo' to she gits good and dark, and den he say, "Let ev'y man take and blow his ram hawn to I tell him to stop." And ev'y man blowed, all night long. And when daylight come, Gideon looked out and seed Baal's army, jest like hit was de night before, only all his men was daid.

"Lawd," say Gideon, "how'd dat come to pass?"

So de Lawd sort of laughed. "Baal's army jest kilt itself," he say. "You see, hit was like dis.

When my men and Baal's men lined up, Baal knowed he had about ten men to my one, and he was r'arin' for a fight. And efn I had marched in at him, us might of got whupped. So I lined up my men and sont half of 'em home, and old Baal seed me do hit.

"Well, dat sort of worried Baal. He knowed he had mo' men den me, and he knowed I knowed it. So he couldn't figure out how come I was sendin' part of my men home.

"So I jest let dat simmer on his mind awhile and den I up and sont some more home. Den old Baal got to figurin' I was up to somethin' which he didn't know about. And de more men I'd send home de more he'd worry. And de more he'd worry de less he wanted to fight. He didn't know efn I had three hund'ed men or three million men, so he jest told his army to git ready for anything which come along.

"So when hit got dark he got so uneasy to when he yared ev'ybody blowin' a ram hawn, he figured no less'n three million men was onto him. So he grab up his swowd and told ev'y man to look out de best way he could.

"Well, hit was dark and they couldn't see who was gittin' stuck, so ev'y man stuck de man

[181]

closest to him, to finally ev'ybody got stuck wid de swowd. And all my army was doin' was standin' back blowin' de ram hawns."

"Well, I be doggone," say Gideon. "Dat sho was a good trick."

"I been workin' dat trick all my life," say de Lawd. "When a man quit me for some yuther god, I don't strike him down. I jest go on like I ain't payin' him no mind, and dat makes him worry. So he jest worries and worries to finally he gits skeered and he strikes hisself down to keep me from doin' hit. Dat's one of my oldest tricks. And hit ain't never failed me yit."

Balaam and His Talking Mule

WELL, hit was hard times in de Promise' Land. And all 'cause de Hebrew chilluns didn't march wid de Lawd. Hit seem like about de time de Lawd got 'em straightened out, well somethin' else would happen. So hit was a war wid de Philistines and all de menfolks was off fightin'. And hit was a man name Balaam which de Cap'm left at home to kind of take keer of old Miz Deborah and keep de enemies from stealin' de hosses and cows and chickens and niggers and things.

Old Balaam went 'long, but purty soon de young niggers got to runnin' off, and de enemies stealed de hosses and cawn and things, to finally hit wa'n't nobody on de place but old Miz Deborah and Balaam and a stove-up old mule name Judy.

"Dis aint gittin' nowheres, Judy," old Balaam tell de mule. "I and you jest natchally got to git out and make a gyarden, or else us ain't gonter do no eatin' round yar, first thing I know."

So old Balaam and old Judy got out to makin' a gyarden, plowin' along and plantin' vegetables. Balaam was a man which liked to do a heap of tawkin', so he didn't had no folks to tawk to, so he tawked to old Judy.

"Git yo' haid outn dem pea vines, Judy," he say. "Us got to eat dem peas next winter and yar you tryin' to eat 'em all now. Git on down de furrer and maybe I'll give you a year of cawn next Sunday."

Well, old Judy yared 'bout dat year of cawn so much and seed so little of hit dat all at once she up and got sick and tired of Balaam's tawk. So one day when old Balaam was tawkin' she turn right around and say to him, high and sassy,

"Whar dat year of cawn you promise' me last Chuesday?"

Well, when Balaam seed dat you could 'a' knocked him down wid a sledge hammer.

"Is dat you tawkin' to me, mule?" he say.

"Hit ain't my shadder," say Judy. "I'm sick and tired of you doin' all de tawkin' round yar and me do de listenin'."

So Balaam and de mule sot down and tawked and tawked about how de crops wa'n't doin' much on account of hit not rainin' much and how hard times hit was cause ev'ybody was fightin' in de war and how de enemies done stole all de cawn and chickens and things.

"Whar deseyar enemies stay at?" say Judy.

"In de woods on de yonder side of town," say Balaam.

"Well," say Judy, "le's I and you sa'nter over dat way and wreak us some havoc among 'em for stealin' all de cawn. I'm gittin' sick and tired of livin' on Jap clover and crab grass. I craves cawn. And I jest kinder b'lieves my old hind laigs is soople enough yit to make myself onderstood in mighty nigh any sassiety."

"You ain't talkin' to me," say Balaam. "De Cap'm left me yar to look after de place and I ain't aimin' to lay down on de Cap'm. Cou'se I ain't skeered. I jest ain't goin'."

So old Judy stuck her haid back in de pea vines and quit tawkin', and all at once a cwoil of smoke sprung up and out stepped de Lawd.

"Balaam," say de Lawd.

"Yas, Lawd," say Balaam.

"I been tawkin' to you by old Judy and you hyared me not. Now I'm tawkin' to you by de fire and smoke, to git yo'se'f on over back of town and whup mine enemies. De white folks had they chance and they ain't gittin' along so good. So I 'p'ints you to go out and whup 'em."

"But, Lawd," say Balaam, "I ain't got no business messin' round de white folkses' fight. Did I go over yonder and tell de white folks how to smite dem enemies, well, de first thing you know I'd be hangin' up on a telephome pole and hit wouldn't be de enemies which done hit. Naw-suh, Lawd. I knows how to git along wid my white folks. Cou'se I kin whup de enemies, all right, but you know how hit is. De white folks is been mighty nice to me and I jest don't want to start no trouble."

"Well," say de Lawd, "I didn't think about

dat part of hit, Balaam. Hit do look kind of tough. But de way de thing figgers out in my plan which I runs de w'l' on, hit ain't no white man a-livin' which kin conquer old Sisera, and hit ain't nobody kin whup de enemies to old Sisera gits conquered. So hit looks like you got to go, even do you has to chin de telephome post along wid yo' yuther troubles."

So Balaam and de Lawd sot and tawked and argyed, and de more they'd argy de more hit looked like old Balaam had to go over to whup de enemies.

"Lawd," say Balaam, "you pass a miracle on old Judy so she kin tawk for herse'f. Dat mule is got more sense den I and you put together."

So de Lawd r'ared back and passed a miracle on Judy and she tuck her haid outn de pea vines and started tawkin'.

"De way I got hit figgered," say Judy, "jest de minute somebody gits close enough to old Gen'l Sisera to kick his slats in, de yuther enemies is ready to quit and go fishin'. 'Cause from what I yars, hit's old Sisera which is puttin' all de yuther boys up to devilment."

"Yeah," say de Lawd, "ev'ybody been knowin' dat all de time. But what us wants to know is,

[187]

how we gonter git close enough to Sisera to git in dat lick? I could do hit myself, could I git close enough to him."

"And," say Balaam, "did you git a kick at him, you would be in a bad shape wid de white folks. Did a mule whup de enemies when de white folks missed, how long you think you'd stay outn de soap factory? Somebody'd be washin' they hands wid you in no time."

"Yeah," say de Lawd, "white folks is funny dat way. When they can't, nobody else needn't try. 'Cause you's soap efn you do."

"You might jest as well stick yo' haid back in de pea vines, Judy," say Balaam, "and let I and de Lawd figger dis thing out."

"Don't y'all worry 'bout my haid in de pea vines, nor neither about me makin' soap. I'll eat grass offn yo' grave, all right. And efn y'all do jest like I tell you, I bet I'll have old Sisera in de dozens in no time, and won't nobody git swang to a telephome pole and won't nobody git made into soap, and ev'ybody'll be happy."

"Well," say de Lawd, "from de looks of things ev'ybody ain't gonter be happy to somebody busts old Sisera, and de cyards say hit ain't a white man gonter live to do hit. So dat leaves

[188]

hit up to you and Balaam. And dat figgers down to chinnin' a telephome pole or makin' soap."

"What do de cyards say about a white woman?" say de mule.

"Don't say," say de Lawd. "But I ain't crazy enough to think a woman gonter whup a big man like Sisera."

"Well," say Judy, "jest give me a chance at hit. Balaam, you go out and fix up a sign which say you got a tawkin' mule which kin tell fawtunes and prophet de weather and advise in love, and I and you will git on over whar de enemies is at."

So Balaam fix de sign and rid old Judy over to de enemies and put up a tent. And hit wa'n't no time to business was good at ten cents a haid. And first thing Balaam know, up wawks a big man in a fancy unifawm and lays down a ten-dollar bill.

"Efn dat mule kin tell me what I want to know," he say, "I don't want no change."

So quick as Judy yared dat, she knowed hit was Sisera.

"Gen'l," say Judy, "ev'y time I looks at yo'

hand I can't see nothin' but a good-lookin' woman."

"Whar is she at?" say Sisera.

"Jest layin' back, jest crazy to meet you," say Judy. "And purty? Lawd! Lawd! And as lonesome as a dawg."

"Whar dat woman at?" say Sisera.

"She 'lows she don't want nothin' less'n a good-lookin' gen'l hangin' round her house."

"Mule," say Sisera, "lead me to dat woman, or else I'm gonter make soap outn yo' rusty hide."

"You jest come along wid I and Balaam," say Judy, "and us leads you."

So Balaam and Sisera got on old Judy and rid on twarg Miz Deborah's house.

"I forgits to tell you," say Judy, "dat dis lady is a married woman and she got a little gal name Jael."

"Married or single," say Sisera, "hit's all de same to me. 'Cause when dat gal sees me she gonter forgit all about her husband."

So old Judy fox-trot along awhile. "She likes a stout man," she say.

"Dat's me," say Sisera. "I'm so stout to I strains myself jest wawkin' round sometime."

"When her husband went off," say Judy, "he

[190]

fixed de front gate mighty tight, so hit'll take a awful stout man to open hit."

"Dat's jest whar I shows her how stout I am," say Sisera. "I opens de gate."

So old Judy fox-trot on up to de gate, and old Sisera gits down to open de gate. And about de time he gits all bunt over to strain at de gate, old Judy wheels round and, ker-blip! You couldn't see nothin' but de print of her hind feet on de seat of old Sisera's pants as he went sailin' through de gate.

"Now, Balaam," say Judy, "you call little Jael out to bring de ax." And when Jael brang de ax, Balaam made her chop old Sisera's haid off, so's he'd be kilt to fulfil de Scriptures, and him and Judy wouldn't git in no trouble wid de white folks.

So 'bout dat time de Cap'm come home and seed little Jael playin' with de ax.

"Balaam," he say, "didn't I told you not to let de baby play wid de ax? Hit looks like ev'y time I turns my back, you let de baby git holt of de ax. She gonter hurt somebody wid hit, first thing I know."

"She done hurted somebody," say Balaam. "Dat big scound'el Sisera was over yar cussin' and

goin' on and she done up and kilt him wid de ax
while I helt him."

"Well, dat's all right den," say de Cap'm.
"Yar's two bits, and you kin knock off and go
to town Sadday evenin'. I b'lieves in bein' good
to my niggers when they behaves theyselves."

Samson, Strong Boy

WELL, de Philistines was a crazy bunch. You could whup 'em, but they wouldn't stay whupped. They was livin' in de Promise' Land, same as de Hebrew chilluns, and they was always quarrelin' and fightin' wid de Hebrew chilluns about who owned de land. And sometimes de Hebrews was ahead and sometimes de Philistines was ahead.

So hit was a man name Samson. And he was a stout man. He wa'n't de kind of man which hung round de store all de time, braggin' 'bout how stout he was, too. He was de kind of man which got out and fit de Philistines, and he was de kind of man which whupped 'em ev'y time he fit 'em.

So one day he was chasin' a bunch of Philistines down de hill when all at once he come up on a line which had a Philistine gal down and was fixin' to eat her up.

"Git offn dat gal, line," say Samson. "Dat ain't no way to treat no lady, even efn she is a Philistine lady."

So de line didn't git, and Samson jest reached over and grabbed him and wrung his neck like a chicken's. So de gal sot up and bat her eyes a couple of times.

"You sho is a stout man," she said. "I bet you's old Samson hisse'f, ain't you?"

"Dat's what de folks calls me," say Samson.

"I knowed hit de minute I laid my eyes on you," say de gal. "I say, 'dat good-lookin' scound'el ain't nobody efn he ain't old Samson.' And I be doggone efn I wa'n't right!"

So Samson kind of stuck out his chist and strained at his arms to de muscles bulged and he strutted a little. "Yeah," he say, "de people call me Samson, and I reckon I'm him."

"And stout!" say de gal. "Lawd! Lawd! De

way you wrung dat line's neck jest sont cold
shivers up my backbone. I never seed such a
man. I's seed a heap of stout men and I's seed
a heap of good-lookin' men. But I ain't never
yit seed a man which was good-lookin' and stout
too, like you is. Not half."

"I'm kinder stout," say Samson, "but I ain't
good-lookin', much."

"Aw, ain't you?" say de gal. "Well, dat line
jest scratched my eyes out. 'Cause efn you ain't
good-lookin', I'm plum blind. And crazy, too."

"You ain't so bad-lookin', yo'se'f, sugar," say
Samson. "What yo' name?"

"Delilah," say de gal. "Hit's a kind of ugly
name, but hit's purty enough for a ugly old gal
like me."

"Yeah?" say Samson. "Hit's a mighty purty
name, but hit ain't as purty as you is."

So they sot and tawked and tawked to finally
and hit wa'n't long to Samson and Delilah was
huntin' for de cou't-house.

"What you gonter do at de cou't-house?" say
de Lawd.

"Gonter git a pair of licenses to marry dis
good-lookin' gal," say Samson.

"Well, I be doggone," say de Lawd.

"Hit's a heap of men will," say Samson, "when I gits dis gal married up wid me."

"Gal, hunh?" say de Lawd. "She's a widder woman, efn I knows what I's tawkin' 'bout."

"I don't keer efn she's a grandma," say Samson; "she looks good to me."

"Well, I ain't de kind of man to meddle wid folks gittin' married," say de Lawd, "but I jest want to ax you one question. How much life insurance is you got?"

"Ain't got none but de gov'ment insurance f'm fightin' in de war," say Samson.

"Well," say de Lawd, "she won't kill you for dat, I reckon. But she sho gonter make you s'port her, 'cause I reckon she done spent de insurance her last husband left her."

"I'm de kind of man which loves to s'port a good-lookin' gal," say Samson.

"Yeah, you's young," say de Lawd. "But you'll learn."

So Samson and Delilah went on and got married up, and when they got home Delilah started bawlin' and cryin'.

"What de matter, baby?" say Samson.

[196]

"I'm skeered," say Delilah. "I hadn't ought to married a big, stout man like you. You might git mad at me and hit me jest once, and kill me."

"I ain't gonter git mad and hit you, gal," say Samson. "I ain't gonter do nothin' but jest hug you a little."

So Delilah bust out cryin' again. "S'posin' you forgits and hugs me wid dem big old arms and mashes me all up," she say.

"Naw, I ain't gonter do nothin' like dat," say Samson. "I ain't gonter hurt you wid my arms."

"I'm skeered you might," she say.

"Listen, sugar," say Samson. "I'm gonter tell you a secret which you ain't to tell nobody. I ain't no stouter in de arms den any yuther man."

"Naw?" say Delilah.

"Naw," say Samson. "Hit's in my hair what makes me so stout. Dat's whar all my strenk is, in my hair. Dat's how come I don't git no haircut. I'm stout in my hair."

"Is dat a fack?" say Delilah. "Well, I ain't so skeered, den, darlin'. Le's have de weddin' supper now."

So at de weddin' supper hit was a heap of wine and old Delilah kept on fillin' Samson's glass to first thing you know Samson was under de table, drunker'n a b'iled owl.

So quick as Samson passed out Delilah told de yuther Philistines and they up and gived old Samson a haircut, and he lost his strenk, and den they jab out his eyes. And before old Samson hardly knowed what had happened, Delilah had him hitched up to de plow like a mule, workin' him in de fields.

Well, all dat happened about plantin' time in de early spring. And old Samson and de mule which was hitch up wid him kept right on plowin' in de field. To when de crops got laid by, and come de Fou'th of July, Delilah hitched old Samson and de mule up to de buggy and driv to town whar de barbecue and speakin' was.

"Well, looky yonder at Delilah," say de Philistine people. "You's de beatin'est gal I ever seed. Got yo' husband hitched up to de buggy wid a mule. Dat ain't old Samson, is hit?"

"Dat's him," say Delilah. "A lady got to git some good outn her husband, so de best way I kin use mine is to make a mule outn him."

So ev'ybody laugh at dat. "You made a fool outn him, you mean," say de Philistines.

"Mule or fool, hit all de same wid me," say Delilah.

So de people kept right on laughin' and passin' remarks about old Samson to finally old Samson got his Af'ican up. "O Lawd," he prayed, "dat woman made a fool outer me. But jest give me my strenk back jest once mo', please, and I'll make a fool outer more of yo' enemies den you kin count."

"Well," say de Lawd, "you ain't de first man a woman done made a fool out of, and you ain't de last. But I don't see how come you axin' me to give yo' strenk back. You ain't had a haircut since early in de spring, and yo' hair is growed out now."

So Samson strained hisself and felt his strenk. "Now look out," he say, and before anybody knowed what was up, he'd done snatched dat mule's jaw bone off and he lit in to de Philistines, and before he got done workin' on 'em he had Philistines stacked up to you couldn't hardly see.

"Looks like about ten thousand," say de Lawd.

"I ain't got time to count 'em, Lawd," say Samson. "All I know is, I got all of 'em which come to de speakin', and now I'm goin' back to git de ones which didn't come out."

Ol' Man Adam an' His Chillun

"Dat's de way I like to yar a man tawk," say de Lawd, "and I b'lieve you'll do hit, 'cause you's blind and won't take after de first good-lookin' woman which makes eyes at you."

Old Man Job

ONE day de Lawd was layin' back in de shade,
watchin' his people, to all at once he seed a man
name Job comin' down de road, singin':

"I look down de road and I seed de devil comin'—
    I know de Lawd done laid his hands on me!
So I tuck off my shoes and I beat de devil runnin'—
    I know de Lawd done laid his hands on me!"

"Hey-ho, Job!" say de Lawd. "You must be mighty happy, wawkin' long, singin' 'bout me like dat."

"Yeah, Lawd," say Job, "I'm a happy man. I got plenty of money, and plenty of land, and plenty of chilluns, and dat's enough to make mighty nigh anybody happy. Den I got you, too, Lawd, which'd make me happy even efn I didn't had nothin' else."

"Well, dat's de way I likes to yar a man tawk," say de Lawd. "When I yars a man tawkin' like dat, I'm gonter stick by him, rain or shine."

"Thanky, Lawd," say Job. "I appreciates yo' stickin' wid me. And I ain't meanin' to brag, onderstand. But I know you's a busy man, Lawd, so as long as I'm gittin' along as good as I am now, you jest needn't worry none 'bout me. You go on and help out somebody which ain't as happy as me, and let me look out for myse'f. But, Lawd, de first time I run into somethin' which I can't handle, I'm gonter git right down on my knees and start hollerin' for help. So jest don't forgit to listen, once in a while."

"All right, Job," say de Lawd. "And de first yip I yars out of you, I'm gonter drap what I'm doin' and come a runnin', too. You won't have to holler twice."

"Well, so long, Lawd," say Job.

"So long, Job," say de Lawd, "and don't forgit to holler do you need some help."

And Job wawked off, singin'.

"Job is what I calls a good man," say de Lawd.

"Say which, Lawd?" Hit was ole Satan standin' right by de Lawd.

"Hey-ho, Satan!" say de Lawd. "I ain't seed you in a month of Sundays. How's Miz Satan and de gals?"

"Finest kind, Lawd," say Satan. "How's all yo' folks?"

"Can't complain," say de Lawd. "Fact is, I'm doin' mighty well dese days and times. Cou'se, some of my people kicks over de traces once in a while. But I can't complain. You see, hit's gittin' to be so many of 'em, to I can't hardly handle 'em all by myself. But I jest names me a preacher yar and yonder to help me out, and we gits along."

"Yeah," say Satan. "Quick as you names a preacher, yar come me and I makes a little tawk wid him, and hit ain't hardly no time to I got

him on my side. Lawd, what you don't know
ain't no skin offn yo' back."

"Yeah?" say de Lawd. "Is dat a fack?"

"Anyways," say Satan, "hit's my plan to work
hit dat way."

"Well," say de Lawd, "yo' plan won't work."

"I'd jest like to bet you a fawty-acre farm,"
say Satan, "dat I kin work hit on any man you
names."

"I ain't no bettin' man," say de Lawd, "but
efn you wants to try yo' hand on somebody, yonder goes ole man Job down de road right now."

"Hit's funny about how dese people won't
bet," say old Satan. "I wonder is you skeered
of losin' fawty acres?"

"I'll jest give you fawty acres," say de Lawd,
"and I'll bet you a ten-cent cigar to make hit
intrustin'."

So Satan went out to whar Job's cattle and
sheep was grazin' and he sent a pack of wolves
to drive 'em off. So de boy come runnin' to de
house, to tell Job.

"Mister Job," say de boy, "wolves done driv
off de cows and sheep."

"Dat's all right," say Job, "jest as long as
nothin' don't happen to de hosses and mules."

So 'bout dat time de stable boy come up and say, "Mister Job de blind staggers done broke out 'mongst de hosses and mules."

"Dat's all right," say Job. "We kin wawk to church, and seein' how cheap cotton is, hit ain't hardly worth de trouble to raise hit, nohow."

So 'bout dat time de house boy come runnin' up. "Mister Job," he say, "de house fell down and killed all de chilluns."

"Did hit kill de ole lady, too?" say Job.

"Nawsuh," say de boy.

"Well," say Job, "de Lawd sont I and de ole lady dem chilluns. And efn de Lawd wants us to have some more, he'll send some more."

So ole Satan seed he wa'n't gittin' nowheres, and he went to de Lawd.

"Lawd," he say, "I ain't de kind of man to crawfish on a bet. But I bet you been tawkin' to Job, 'cause I done him dirdy ev'y way I kin think of, and he ain't moved a peg."

"I ain't said a word to him," say de Lawd, "nor him to me. And I likes my cigars long and yaller."

So de devil sot and scratched his haid and thunk. To finally he made up his mind. "I hates to do hit," he say, "but I ain't aimin' to let de Lawd win dat cigar after all de braggin' I done."

So dat night when Job was sleepin', de devil made a pass over him, and de next mawnin' Job got up wid a stiff knee.

"Ole lady," he say, "I feel like I got a bile on my knee."

"Hit looks like a carbuncle to me," say Miz Job.

"Well, le's put a little muley ointment on hit," say Job. And he did, but de carbuncle kept on spreadin', and a new one would break out.

"Man," say Miz Job, "git outn dis house. I'm sick and tired of yo' moanin' round yar."

"Well," say Job, "de Lawd give me dese carbuncles, and he give me dis house, so I reckon I'll stay round some."

"You got another reckon comin'," say Miz Job. "Git out in de ash hopper. I has yared dat ashes was good for carbuncles."

"Well," say Job, "de Lawd give me dat ash hopper, too." So he went out and got in de ash hopper, and hit look like ev'y time he'd roll over a new carbuncle would spring up on him.

"De Lawd sho is generous," say Job. "When

he give me stock he give me a heap, and when he give me chilluns he give me a plenty, and when he give me carbuncles, he give me about all one man kin handle. Blessed be de name of de Lawd, 'cause he ain't stingy."

So things went on, and first thing Job knows his head deacon, name ole man Bildad, come over to see how he's gittin' along.

"I yar you been ailin', Brother Job," say Bildad, "so I brang dese flowers over to you. They's lilies and I figgered efn I got yar too late, they'd come in handy at de funeral."

"Un-hunh," say Job. "We been havin' some nice weather, ain't we?"

"Jest right for a funeral," say Bildad. "I hates to go to a funeral in de rain."

"You sho sounds happy, Bildad," say Job.

"Well, I got ev'ything worked out," say Bildad. "I done arranged for a preacher to preach de funeral when you leaves us, so you don't has to worry 'bout dat. We gonter give you a fine funeral."

"Well, good-by, Brother Bildad," say Job. "I hope you don't come back to cheer me up no more."

"Naw, I guess you'll be in glory when I gits back," say Bildad. "I hope yo' crown won't rest too heavy on dat carbuncle on yo' forehaid."

So Bildad went on, and Job lays back down in de ashes, and ev'y time he turns over he gits a new carbuncle.

So he started to raise up his haid to tawk about how generous de Lawd is wid ev'ything he do, and a sharp pain tuck him right square back of de neck.

"Dar now," say Job, "I be doggone efn de Lawd ain't put a carbuncle on de back of my neck! Dat's jest too many. Hit whups me."

So ole Job didn't waste no time. He got right down on his knees, right in de ashes.

"O Lawd," he say, "yar I is in de ash hopper, stricken down wid de carbuncles. Lawd, thou gavest me a heap of sheep and cows and thou tuck 'em away. And I said 'Amen.' Lawd, thou gavest me a heap of mules and hosses and thou tuck 'em away. And I said 'Amen.' Thou gavest me and de ole lady a heap of purty chilluns, and thou tuck 'em away. And I said 'Amen.' Lawd, thou sent a heap of carbuncles on me, and when you gits ready to take 'em away

I knows you gonter, and I'm gonter say 'Amen.' Thou sent ole man Bildad over yar to devil me, and thou sent him away, and I praised yo' name. So you see, Lawd, good or bad, I'm sayin' 'Amen' to ev'ything you do, 'cause I know's you's right.

"Now, Lawd, I ain't complainin'. But when I was a young man I went down in de valley and I found you, and I started followin' you, and I been followin' you ev'y since. Sometimes I stumbles, Lawd, and sometimes I falls down. But I always gits back on my feet and takes out after you again. When I come to de ditch of trouble, I jump over efn I kin, Lawd, and efn I can't jump hit, I wades. But jump or wade, Lawd, I'm right after you, never askin' no questions and never askin' no help.

"Lawd, when you put dat carbuncle on my knee I kept right on comin'. You put one on my back, and I didn't slow down. You plastered one on my shoulder, and I halted not. You spread one across my forehaid, but I jest shet my eyes and kept a-travelin'.

"But, Lawd, when you plastered dat thing on de back of my neck, I jest got to holler, 'Calf rope.' Hit whupped me. I got to quit, Lawd,

'cause I can't travel no more by myse'f. So I'm
axin' you right yar and now, Lawd, to come
and give me yo' hand and help me out of my
troubles."

So de Lawd stepped up to de ash hopper and
say, "Well, Job, jest like I told you, quick as
you holler for me, yar I am. Now what is hit
you's wantin'?"

So Job p'inted to de back of his neck. "Dis
carbuncle, Lawd," he say.

"I don't see no carbuncle, Job," say de Lawd.

Job put his hand on his neck and grinned,
"You done tuck hit away, Lawd," he say.
"Much oblige'."

"Yeah, Job," say de Lawd. "I tuck 'em all
away, and I brang you back yo' cows and sheeps
and chilluns and things. And yar is a ten-cent
cigar to boot. Now go on back to yo' preachin'."

"Thanky, Lawd," say Job. "And, Lawd, I
wonder is you got anybody in mind which'll
make a good head deacon?"

"What de matter wid Brother Bildad?" say de
Lawd. "He was de head deacon de last time I
yared about hit."

"Yeah," say Job, "he was head deacon. But
he ain't, no more."

So de Lawd laugh. "I wouldn't be too hard on Bildad," he say. "He's all right. I put him up to comin' over yar. Hit was all a part of de way I got of runnin' my yearth. Bildad is all right."

Little David

WELL, de Hebrews whupped de Philistines and
de Philistines whupped de Hebrews. But neither
side wouldn't stay whupped. So finally de Lawd
sort of got tired stayin' round to he'p out de
Hebrews all de time, so he app'inted a man name
King Saul to be king er de Hebrews.

"King Saul," say de Lawd, "you take and lead
my people while I go on back and 'tend to my
angels a little."

Ole King Saul was a purty good king when
hit come to fightin', but when hit come to jest
plain ev'yday kingin', ole Saul wa'n't so much.

But as long as he whupped de Philistines de people hung wid him, and sort of put up wid him for de rest er de time. So Saul started to think he was purty good all de way round.

"What a king needs," say ole King Saul, "is a heap er music round de camp." So he sont out and got a little boy name Little David to come and play on his harp round de camp.

Little David was one er deseyar boys which could do mighty nigh anything and could do hit good. But when hit come right down to hit, he could make up songs and sing 'em better'n he could do anything else. He always was makin' up a song and playin' hit on his harp and singin'. Even while he was out herdin' his daddy's sheep he'd take and put his harp in his pocket and set out on de hillside and sing:

"Ef I could I sholy would,
    I wanter stand on de rocks whar Moses stood.
    Little David, play on yo' harp, hallelu! hallelu!
    Little David, play on yo' harp, hallelu!"

So while he was singin' a big bear come and stole a sheep and he had to git up and run de bear down to git de sheep back. Den he went on back and sung some mo':

[213]

"Old Joshua was de son of Nun,
    And he never quit fightin' to de fightin' was done.
    Little David, play on yo' harp, hallelu! hallelu!
    Little David, play on yo' harp, hallelu!"

So 'bout dat time yar come a line and stole another sheep, so Little David had to git up and run him down.

"Dis ain't gittin' nowheres," he say. "I'm gittin' sick and tired er runnin' deseyar thievin' varmints down ev'y time they steals a sheep. I bet I'm gonter fix me somethin' which'll do my runnin' for me." So he tuck and cut de tongue outer his shoe and got two strings and make him a sling-shot. So he set down and started singin' again:

"Old Joshua stood on de top er de hill,
    And he looked at de sun and de sun stood still.
    Little David, play on yo' harp, hallelu! hallelu!
    Little David, play on yo' harp, hallelu!"

So 'bout dat time a wolf come up and steal hisse'f a sheep. But David didn't git up and run after him. He jest got a rock and put hit in de sling-shot and slung hit round his head about twice, and ker-blip! de wolf thought de lightnin' had done struck him!

So when ole King Saul sont for Little David,

Little David

Little David not only tuck 'long his harp, but he tuck 'long his sling-shot, too. So one day he was settin' out in front of ole King Saul's tent, playin' and singin' away, to all at once hit started to git dark and de yearth started to tremble and de ground started to shake.

"What dat, ole King Saul?" say Little David.

"Dat's ole Goliar," say old King Saul.

"Who he?" say David.

"De he-coon er de Philistines," say King Saul.

"What do he want?" say David.

"Trouble," say ole King Saul.

"Well, you de king, ain't you?" say Little David. "Can't you ease his worries 'long dat line?"

"Who, me?" say Saul. "I'm a married man. Cou'se I ain't skeered of him, but still and at de same time I got a wife and a family dependin' on me for s'port. So I don't see no reason how come I should git out and git hurted by no gi'nt."

"He's a gi'nt?" say Little David.

"Twenty foot tall," say King Saul.

"What else is he?" say David.

"Jest wait to he gits out in de clearin' and starts makin' his say-so," say King Saul.

So 'bout dat time ole Goliar stepped out in de clearin' and commenced makin' his say-so.

"I'm a cross betwixt a wild cat and de yaller ianders," he say. "I'm sired by Trouble and dammed by Sudden Death. I drinks nothin' but stump water and a rattlesnake bit me and died. I breathes out forked lightnin' and I spits out thunder. When I laughs de skies pop open, and when I groans hit rolls up like a ball er yarn. I kills my friends and I makes hamburgers outer my enemies. Tornadoes and harrycanes follow me round like pet dogs, and lines and tigers is my playmates. I'm bad. I'm mean. I'm vicious, and jest natchally can't he'p it. When I gits sick hit takes nothin' less'n a Hebrew man's meat to cyore me. And I feel a buck auger comin' on. So look out! I'm reekin' wid meanness and I'm huntin' trouble."

"Sounds hard, don't he?" say Little David.

"Sounds?" say ole King Saul. "Son, dat big scound'el is hard!"

"Is you skeered of him?" say Little David.

"Naw, I ain't skeered of him," say ole King Saul, " 'cause I got sense enough to keep outn his way."

"I ain't skeered of him," say Little David.

[216]

"You kin run purty fast, kin you?" say Saul.

"Naw, I ain't de runnin' kind," say Little David. "I'm jest goin' up yonder and whup dat sound'el befo' supper time."

"You gonter which?" say ole King Saul.

"I'm gonter whup him," say Little David, "or else he gonter whup me."

"Well," say ole King Saul, "be keerful and don't meet up wid de ole Fool Killer on yo' way over, 'cause efn de Fool Killer meet up wid you, he gonter beat ole Goliar to you."

Little David didn't said a word. He jest tuck his harp in one hand and his sling-shot in de yuther, and he went off singin':

"When I gits to heaven I'm gonter be like Job.
I'm gonter wawk all around in my long, white robe.
Little David, play on yo' harp, hallelu! hallelu!
Little David, play on yo' harp, hallelu!"

So when ole Goliar seed Little David he say, "What you doin' over yar on my side, little ole Hebrew boy?"

"I thought I yared somebody say you was lookin' for trouble," say Little David.

"Don't play wid me, little boy," say Goliar. "I'm in a bad humor and I ain't kilt me no Hebrew since yistiddy. Trot 'long back home befo'

I gits mad and spatters you up ag'in' de side er de yearth."

"You don't want to fight wid me?" say Little David. "I yared 'bout deseyar boys wid de big say-so, and f'm what I yars, hit's all say-so and no do-so."

Well, dat made old Goliar good and hot, so he arch up his back and squnch down his shoulders and start stiff-laiggin' round and roarin' and bellowin'. "I'm comin', so jest watch out for me," he say. "I'm dealin' death and destruction right yar and now." And he dance stiff-laigged round Little David, jest groanin' and gruntin' like hit's hurtin' him powerful bad to hold hisse'f back to he gits done wid his dancin' and tawkin'.

"I'm comin', 'cause I can't hold myse'f back no longer," say ole Goliar and he started twarg Little David.

So Little David jest drap a rock into his sling-shot and slung hit round his head, and ker-blop! he tuck ole Goliar right between de eyes and ole Goliar never knowed what hit him.

So 'bout dat time de Lawd stepped out f'm behind a bush and say: "Well, dat settles hit, Little David. You gonter be king over my people."

[218]

"Aw, Lawd," say Little David, "ole King Saul is de king."

"You mean he was de king," say de Lawd. "I been holdin' on to him 'cause he makes out like he kin fight. But you not on'y kin sing, but you kin outfight him, too, and ev'ybody knows ole King Saul can't sing. So hit's jest like I say, son. You de king, and no argyment wid me 'bout hit."

"Well, thanky, Lawd," say Little David. So he picks up his harp and wawked on back to camp, singin':

"Little David was a shepherd's boy,
And he killed ole Goliar and he hollered wid joy.
Little David, play on yo' harp, hallelu! hallelu!
Little David, play on yo' harp, hallelu!"

*T*he Mantle of Saul

WELL, when Little David whupped ole Goliar and de Lawd named him king, Little David was de king. But hit seem like when he got back to camp, ole King Saul ain't yared de news yit. So hit got to be a argyment betwixt Saul and David.

"Hit don't make no diff'unce to me, one way or de yuther," say Little David. "But de Lawd say I'm de king, and you say you de king, so hit look like hit's you and de Lawd as to which is right and which is wrong."

So ole King Saul tuck and hurled a javelin at David and David jest ducked in time. And when he ducked he picked hisse'f up a rock and drap hit into his sling-shot.

"Look out wid dat sling-shot, son," say ole King Saul. "I was jest playin' wid you."

"I ain't playin' wid you," say Little David, and he kept on fixin' his sling-shot.

"Dat's all right, son," say Saul. "Efn de Lawd say you's a king, I ain't de kind er man to go 'sputin' wid de Lawd."

"Well, dat's de way I likes to yar a man tawk," say Little David.

"What did de Lawd say you gonter be king of, son?" say Saul.

Well, David wa'n't lookin' for nothin' like dat, so hit had him in de dozens. "Didn't say," Little David allowed, "but I got a mighty good idee what I'm gonter be king of." And he kept monkeyin' round wid de rock.

"I speck," say ole King Saul, "de Lawd aimed for you to be de king over some er de young folks like yo'se'f. So you jest take a few er my young soldiers out and march 'em round de woods and king over 'em."

Well, David wa'n't lookin' for no trouble, so

dat about suited him. So he tuck de young soldiers and marched 'em round de woods awhile.
To purty soon he run short er rations.

"Dis ain't gittin' us nowheres," he tell de soldiers. "I don't keer how much a man is de king,
he ain't gonter have no good time onless he's gittin' his vittles regular, too."

"Ain't it de truf, Yo' Majesty?" say de soldiers.

"Well," say King David, "I'm gonter go over
yonder to dat house and see kin I stir up some
rations." So King David wawked up to de house
and knocked on de door.

"Who knockin'?" say a man.

"King David," say David. "Who is you?"

"My name is Nabal," say de man, and he
opened de door. "What you want?"

"I got my army down yonder in de shade," say
King David, "and us is kinder hongry. So I
thought maybe efn de ole lady had any grub left
over f'm breakfus, she might give us some."

"Yeah, us got a heap er grub left over," say
Nabal's wife.

"Git back in de kitchen, woman," say Nabal.
"Dis boy ain't no king. He ain't got on no crown
and he ain't got on no robe. He don't look like
nothin' but a tramp to me." And den he look

square in David's eye and say, "Naw, you can't have no grub."

"My army," say King David, "been watchin' over yo' sheep and keepin' de wolves outer de flocks."

"I'd jest as leave have de wolves in 'em as you," say Nabal, and he slammed de door right in King David's face.

"I guess I didn't tawk right," say David. "Maybe efn I could tawk to dat good-lookin' wife er hisn, maybe I c'd git some grub." So he wawked round to de kitchen and knocked on de door.

"Lady, won't you please ——" he started to say, but de lady sort of giggles and say, "My name is Abigail, Yo' Majesty. You kin call me dat, efn you wants to."

"Dat sho is a purty name," say King David. "I might er knowed a good-lookin' gal like you'd have a purty name like unto dat."

"Aw, shet up, Yo' Majesty, and go on and eat disyar pie," say Abigail. "Cou'se hit ain't much good, 'cause I made hit myse'f. But some folks likes hit right well."

So David tuck a bite er pie and say, "Hit sho is good, but I b'lieve I'd druther have a bite er dat meat fust, and sort of save de pie for dessert."

"I knowed you was a hard man," say Abigail. "Wantin' to eat meat instid er pie. My husband ain't hard. He likes pie and efn I'd let him, he wouldn't eat nothin' else but pie all de time."

"Sho nuff?" say King David. "How many pieces er dis pie do you speck he'd eat efn you jest turned him loose?"

"He'd eat his fool se'f plum to death," say Abigail.

"How many pies like dis you got in de house?" say David.

"About fawty," say Abigail.

So David sot dar and studied and looked at Abigail. "A good-lookin' gal like you ought to let her ole husband eat all fawty of 'em efn he want to. And what happen to him when he gits done ain't none er yo' rat-killin'."

"You's de fastest man, Yo' Majesty," say Abigail. "You sho kin make a married gal like me change her mind."

"De womenfolks ain't got no time for a little ole king like me," say King David. "Ev'y since I killed ole Goliar and whupped de Philistines and got made king, hit seems like de ladies sort of lost intrust in me. I can't do nothin' but whup de Philistines, and kill de gi'nts, and play on de harp a little, and sing some, and ev'y now and den I writes a psa'm or kills a line. Hit ain't nothin' 'bout me which de womenfolks likes."

"Jest settin' up dar tawkin' wid yo' mouf, Yo' Majesty, you good-lookin' scound'el," say Abigail. "I'm a woman, myse'f, and I'm yar to tell you you got my mind changed quick as I looked at you."

King David reached over and patted her head a little and kissed her in de mouf, and say, "Aw, gal, I b'lieves you's jest funnin' me to make me ashame'."

So Abigail kissed him back and say, "You jest come back tomorrow after my husband gits done eatin' dem fawty pies which I feeds him tonight for supper."

So de next day King David come back and him and Abigail went to ole Nabal's funeral. So when dey was wawkin' 'long home, David tole her all about how he come to be de king and how ole King Saul was argyin' 'bout hit.

"He been huntin' for me ev'y since I marched off wid his soldiers," say King David.

"I bet efn he know what good for him," say

[225]

Abigail, "I bet he's hopin' he can't find you, too."

So dey wawked along to purty soon yar come one er David's soldiers up and say, "King David, ole King Saul is out yar lookin' for you. But he muster got tired, 'cause he done laid down and went to sleep."

"Is dat a fack?" say King David. "Well, I guess you better lead My Majesty to whar he sleepin'."

So de soldier led him to a cave and, sho nuff, yar was ole King Saul layin' back wid his haid on a rock, snorin' away.

"Shall I stick de swowd through him, Yo' Majesty?" say de soldier. "Or maybe I jest better take dis big rock and mash his haid."

"Don't tech him," say King David. "I ain't wantin' to kill ole King Saul. I married two or three of his daughters one time, and hit's ag'in' de law to kill yo' daddy-in-law when he's asleep, even efn he is de king."

So David tuck ole Saul's king-robe and put hit on his own shoulders and he tuck and put de crown on his own haid, and den he stand back and holler, "Wake up, King Saul, wake up!"

So Saul rolled over and opened his eyes. **And**

dar stood David wid de king-robe on his shoulders and de crown on his haid.

"Hello, King David!" say King Saul. "I been huntin' for you mighty nigh ev'ywheres."

"Yeah, so I been yarin'," say King David.

"Yeah," say King Saul. "I been wantin' to give you dat robe and crown. I'm gittin' tired er bein' king. Hit ain't so much fun, anyways." So he sort of grins, sick-like, and rolls over on his own sword and dies. And f'm dat time on King David was de king.

The Adulteration of Old King David

OLE King David made a mighty king. He always had his armies out fightin' for de Lawd, and he was always busy at home, holdin' cou't and keepin' de womenfolks straightened out.

Well, one day ole King David was settin' on de front po'ch, jest settin' back, smokin' a cigar and lettin' his dinner settle. He was a mighty king, but he acted jest like a natchal man, too.

So purty soon a messenger rid up and bowed down to de ground and say, "Yo' Majesty King David, de enemies er de Lawd is done whupped."

"Who say de enemies er de Lawd is whupped, messenger?" say David.

"De General say dey's whupped," say de messenger.

"Well, I don't b'lieve hit," say ole King David. "Dem enemies er de Lawd is a awful pack of liars, and I speck they git de General to say they's whupped jest so's our boys won't fly in and give 'em a sho-'nuff whuppin'. So you jest up and ride back and tell our boys to light into de enemies ag'in and stay lit to dey hollers, 'Calf rope.' "

So de messenger went ridin' off and ole King David r'ared back ag'in, smokin' his cigar and settlin' his dinner.

Well, David was a king and a mighty king. But David was a man, jest like any yuther man. And whar you see a man, hit's bound to be a woman hangin' round somewheres close by. So right across de road was de house of a woman named Miz Uriah.

Miz Uriah was one er deseyar married womens which is good-lookin' and don't keer who knows hit. She's jest de kind dat's always waitin' for her husband to git outer de house so's she kin start messin' round.

Her husband was in de armies er de Lawd, fightin' de enemies, and he left her home to look after de chickens and things while he gone. But dat gal ain' studdin' no chickens. She's got her mind on de menfolks.

And while ole King David is tawkin' to de messenger, she's hidin' behind de window blinds, a-watchin'. And soon as she see de messenger leave, she runs back and puts on her Sunday dress and goes over to whar ole King David is settin'.

"Good mawnin', King David, Yo' Majesty," she say, sweetenin' up her voice.

"Good mawnin', sister," say ole King David. "What can I do for you dis mawnin'?"

"Well," say Miz Uriah, casual-like, "I comed over to ax you does you yar somethin' 'bout my husband. He ain't much husband, but he bet-ter'n no husband a-tall. I guess he's about all a ugly ole gal like me kin git, anyway. I wish I was a good-lookin' gal."

"You don't look so bad, gal," say ole King David.

"Aw, hysh up, Yo' Majesty," say Miz Uriah. "You know I ain't no good-lookin' gal. Jest look at 'at ole ugly laig. Look at 'at flat chest——" and she started twistin' herse'f round, showin' off.

But David is a good man and he know what she's up to, so he say: "Git on back home, gal, befo' I puts you in jail for tryin' to adulterate My Majesty. Git home! You yar me?"

Well, Miz Uriah got on back 'cross de road and ole King David sets down and writes a psa'm 'bout how he resisted temptation. But dat woman ain't started on him yit. She goes on 'cross de road and back in de house, and den de fust thing ole King David know, he sees her draggin' a big washtub out on de front po'ch and start pourin' water in hit.

"Gonter do some washin' today, Sister Uriah?" say ole King David.

"Some, Yo' Majesty," she say.

"I thought you washed yo' clothes on Monday," say de king.

"I does, Yo' Majesty," say Miz Uriah.

"Today's Sadday," say ole King David.

[231]

"I ain't said I was gonter wash no clothes to-day, Yo' Majesty," say Miz Uriah. "Dis is my bath day." And dat gal starts undressin' right out on de front po'ch, right in front er ole King David.

"Whyn't you git back in dat house to git naked, gal?" say ole King David. "You ain't got a lick er sense. S'pose somebody come down de road and sees you?"

"S'pose'n they does," says Miz Uriah. "They won't see nothin' but ole ugly me." And she went right on takin' off her clothes.

Ole King David set and watched her to de last stitch fell off and she stepped in de tub.

"Gal!" say ole King David, "ain't you got no shame? Whyn't you git back in dat house? Standin' out yar naked as a jay bird! Somebody comin' down dat road and see you, fust thing you know."

So Miz Uriah says, kinder baby-like: "Maybe you's right, Yo' Majesty, and I'm is mighty ashame'. But I can't tote dis tub back in de house all by myse'f. Efn Yo' Majesty'll he'p me tote hit in, I'll git back in de house."

Well, yar was ole King David tryin' to keep de kingdom f'm gittin' scandalized by dis fool gal takin' a bath on de front po'ch, and so hit wa'n't nothin' for him to do but go on and he'p her tote de tub back in de house. So he gits up and goes over to he'p her tote de tub back in de house, and dat's de last anybody seed of ole King David to Monday mawnin', when de Lawd come wawkin' up and seed him settin' out on his own front po'ch ag'in, lookin' mighty sad and sinful.

"Heyho, King David!" say de Lawd. "Been writin' any mo' psa'ms since I been round yar?"

"I writ one," say ole King David, "all 'bout how I was resistin' temptation f'm a fool woman."

"Dat sounds good," say de Lawd. "Wait'll I git settled down in dis cheer, and I wants you to read it at me."

"Can't," say ole King David. "I done tored hit up."

So de Lawd and ole King David sot on de po'ch, jest leanin' back and sayin' nothin', to finally yar come Miz Uriah draggin' her washtub out on de front po'ch ag'in, and pourin' water in hit.

Ole King David spotted her and he tried to signal to her to git back in de house, 'cause de Lawd was dar, but she didn't pay him no mind.

She jest kept right on pourin' water in de tub. Den when she got de water in de tub, she brought out a bundle er clothes and started washin' 'em.

"Gonter do some washin', sister?" say de Lawd.

"Yes, Lawd. Monday's my regular washday," she say.

Den de Lawd turn to ole King David and say, "Dat's a mighty fine-lookin' neighbor you got over yonder. What's her name?"

"Dat's Uriah's wife," say King David.

"You mean hit's Uriah's widder," say de Lawd.

"Uriah's which?" say de king.

"Widder," say de Lawd. "Ole Uriah got mixed up wid one er my enemies, and when they got done wid him they had to haul him off in a sack."

"Naw?" say ole King David. "So she's a widder woman! Well I be doggone!" So he got up and started back in de house.

"Whar you goin' now, King David?" say de Lawd.

"To git my pencil and paper," say ole King David. "I'm gonter write another psa'm."

The Wisdom of King Solomon

OLE King David was a king which liked to have
a heap er chilluns runnin' round de house. And
hit seem like ev'y one er his chillun wanted to be
king. So 'bout de time one of 'em up and said
he wanted to be de king 'cause he's de oldest, hit
seem like a bunch of hard luck happened to him
and he died. And den de next oldest boy on deck
had some hard luck, and right on down de line.
But hit was one er de boys name Solomon which
ain't sayin' a word 'bout bein' de king. He jest

went on and studied his books and kept his mouf shet.

"Dat boy Solomon," King David tole de Lawd one day, "is makin' some mighty good marks in school. He liable to grow up to be a lawyer some er dese days."

"Cou'se he's makin' good marks," say de Lawd. "Dat boy got a haid on him as long as a mule, right now, and efn he keeps hit up and don't go runnin' round wid de gals too much, I got somethin' in my mind about him."

So de yuther brothers kept fightin' 'mongst theyse'ves about which is gonter be king when David dies, so when David died Solomon up and put on de crown and de robe and he was king. And Solomon was a smart king, too.

Well, about de fust thing Solomon happened up against was two ladies fightin' over a baby which got mixed up in de hospital or somethin'.

"Dat's my young'n," say one er de ladies.

"Ain't no sich yo' young'n," say de yuther lady. So dey argyed and fought to finally ole King Solomon yared de news and he sont for de ladies to appear before him.

Well, Solomon sot back on de throne and

looked at de baby and den he looked at de ladies.
And den he looked back at de baby again.

"Well," he said, "f'm de way things looks to
me, y'all ladies ain't got no call to raise no ruckus
'bout dis young'n. Y'all is bofe what I'd call
good-lookin' ladies, now ain't you?" So bofe de
ladies kinder giggled back at Solomon. "Yeah,"
say ole King Solomon, "y'all is what I call a couple of right purty gals. And I jest be doggone
efn I kin see how purty gals like y'all kin go to
scrappin' about dis bald-haided little ole brat
which looks like a peeled onion in de face."

So one er de ladies kinder grinned and say,
"Yo' Majesty, he ain't so turrible much to look
at, now, is he?" But de yuther lady jest sot back
and simmered and b'iled.

"Well, what you got to say?" King Solomon
ax de yuther lady.

"Yo' Majesty," say de yuther lady, "you is de
king and long may you wave. But scusin' dat,
you ain't nothin' but a fresh little ole country
boy wid a crown on yo' haid and nothin' in hit.
Somebody tole me you was smart, and I bet de
Lawd done struck 'em down right now for lyin'.
You may be de king, but I bet de fust time you
meet up wid de Fool Killer I bet hit's gonter be

a big funeral and another king, 'long 'bout dat time. You's settin' on de throne wid yo' robe of purple wropped about you, actin' high and mighty, but you ain't foolin' me. I knows po' white trash when I sees 'em. And when I looks at you, I sho kin see 'em."

"You don't like me much, does you?" say ole King Solomon.

"I don't like you a-tall," say de yuther lady. "You don't know nothin' 'bout kingin' and you don't know nothin' 'bout babies. And you don't know nothin' 'bout nothin'. Come yar tellin' me dat dis purty little baby look like a peeled onion! Humph! You may be de king, but you looks like a goggled-eyed bullfrog peepin' through de ice, to me."

"Woman," say King Solomon, "does you mean to say you thinks disyar baby is sho-'nuff purty?"

"I don't think nothin' 'bout hit," say de yuther woman. "I knows hit."

"Dat settle de argyment, den," say ole King Solomon. "Any lady which kin stand flat-footed and say a nine-day-old baby is purty is bound to be de baby's maw. So take him and git."

And den ole King Solomon turn round and

look at de yuther woman and say: "Looky yar, gal. What you mean by claimin' dat woman's baby? Don't you know hit's ag'in' de law to do dat? Hit look like to me you's tryin' to contempt my cou't."

"Naw, I ain't, Yo' Majesty," say de woman. "Hit jest seem like hit's gittin' to be de style dese days and times for ev'y lady to has a baby, and me, I'm so ugly I ain't even got me no husband yit."

"Who say you's ugly, gal?" say King Solomon.

"I said hit," say de lady.

"Well, I got purty good jedgment 'bout de womenfolks," say Solomon, "and I jedges you to be about de best-lookin' gal which is come into my cou't dis week. What's yo' name?"

"My name de Queen of Sheba," say de lady, "but most er my friends jest call me Sheba for shawt."

"Well, doggone my ole rusty hide!" say Solomon. "So you's Sheba, is you? I been yarin' 'bout how good-lookin' you is, and I be dog efn I don't believe hit now. Stand round dar in de light so My Majesty kin git a good look at you. Dad blame my skin! Gal, you's jest so purty you jest won't do!"

"You's kinder handsome yo' ownse'f, ole King Solomon," say de Queen of Sheba. "Most smart men like you is kinder ugly, but you sho ain't."

"Is dat a fack?" say King Solomon. So they sot dar and chinned awhile about de weather and de crops, and fust one thing and another, to finally they got to tawkin' 'bout how smart ole King Solomon was.

"I jest natchally can't he'p bein' smart," say ole King Solomon. "Hit was bawn in me, I reckon. Jest ax me a question, now, and see what I kin do to hit. I ain't braggin', onderstand, but jest ax me one."

"All right," say Sheba, "but I'm liable to make hit a purty hard one. Tell me who's de father er de Zebedee chilluns?"

"Ole man Zebedee," say Solomon, quick as lightnin'.

"Doggone!" say Sheba. "You is a smart scound'el, ain't you, Yo' Majesty?"

"Ax me another question," say ole King Solomon. "I ain't braggin', but I'm brim-full er wisdom and I craves to scatter some about."

"All right," say Sheba. "How come hit wa'n't no seven-up games on de ark?"

[240]

" 'Cause ole Noah was settin' on de deck," say Solomon.

"Ain't you de smartest man!" say Sheba. "I ain't gonter ax you no more."

"Aw, come and ax me," say Solomon. "Ax me, woman."

"Well," say Sheba, "whar was Moses when de lights went out?"

"In de dark," say Solomon.

"All right, what did Adam and Eve do when Abel got kilt?" say Sheba.

"Raised Cain," say Solomon.

"You's too many for me, Yo' Majesty," say Sheba. "Any good-lookin' king wid all yo' brains in his haid is liable to change my mind. I better not ax you no more."

"Aw, come on, sugar, ax me one more," say Solomon.

"Naw suh!" say Sheba. "You got too many brains for a little ole country gal like me."

"Aw, come on, baby," say King Solomon. "Jest ax My Majesty one more."

"Well, I knows you got de answer to dis one," say Sheba, "but I'm gonter ax you hit, jest de same. Who is de smartest and de best-lookin' king in dis man's town?"

"He de king," say ole King Solomon, "which is settin' yar makin' his eyes at de purties' and smartes' queen in dis man's town or any yuther man's town, and he don't keer who knows hit."

So they sot around and tawked awhile, and finally ole King Solomon tuck and built a temple and when he died he had nine hund'ed and ninety-nine wives scattered 'bout de place.

Green Pastures

AFTER ole King Solomon died de kings got to comin' and goin' so fast to hit made de Lawd dizzy tryin' to keep up wid who was de king and who wa'n't de king. So he say, "Dis ain't gittin' nowheres. Ef my people can't keep a king long enough for me to git acquainted wid him, well, I'm gonter see what gonter happen."

So hit was a king over in de next town name Nebuchadnezzar which yared de news, so he say, "Well, when de Lawd was sidin' wid de Hebrew boys they was doin' some mighty struttin'. But now wid de Lawd layin' back and watchin', I'll jest drap over and raise me some sand." And so he did.

So ole King Nebuchadnezzar lined up his army and lit out.

"Halt, who comin' yar?" say de Hebrew sentry.

"Sad news is comin' yar," say King Nebuchadnezzar.

"Ain't yo' name King Nebuchadnezzar?" say de sentry.

"Dat's what dey calls me," he say. "What's yo' name?"

"Daniel," say de sentry.

"Well, Daniel," say Nebuchadnezzar, "I'm bringin' you some sad news. I'm bringin' you de news which say I'm gonter raise me some sand in dis town."

"You better let dis town alone," say Daniel. "When you raise a ruckus in dis town you's raisin' a ruckus in de Lawd's town."

"I kotched de Lawd away f'm home, dis time," say Nebuchadnezzar.

"You didn't kotch me away f'm home," say Daniel.

[244]

"Naw," say Nebuchadnezzar, "and I'm gonter use you. I'm gonter feed my pet lines on you."

So de soldiers captured Daniel and de army marched into town and raised a ruckus. They got drunk and they shot up de place. Den when de sheriff tried to arrest 'em, dey locked de sheriff up in his own jail and den burned de jail down wid him in hit. So they busted out de window lights and they tore down de gyarden fences. So they driv off de men and women and scared all de chillun.

"King Nebuchadnezzar," say Queen Nebuchadnezzar when he got back home, "did you spile dat town?"

"Did I spile hit?" say de king. "Queen Nebuchadnezzar, I didn't spile hit, I jest natchally ruint hit."

"Well, did you bring me somethin' back?" say de queen.

"I brang back some solid-gold drinkin' cups, and I brang back a few Hebrew boys to feed my lines on," he say.

"You's always bringin' back somethin' to drink out of, and somethin' to feed yo' lines on," say de queen, "but you ain't brang back nothin' to build me no fire wid. And yar poor me, settin' round de house queenin' all day long and 'bout to freeze to death."

"Well, queen," say de king. "I'm good-hearted. You kin have a few of my Hebrew boys to pitch on de fire."

So dey brought out a few of de Hebrew boys and pitch 'em on de fire. But when dey got to doin' de Hebrew boys like dat, de Lawd tuck a hand. "Jest go on and git pitched in de fire," say de Lawd, " 'cause I ain't gonter let you git burnt." So when dey put de Hebrews in de fire hit jest sputtered a couple er times and went out.

"No wonder they won't burn," say King Nebuchadnezzar; "you ain't got no kindlin' in yar." So dey brang a armful of pine knots and toch off. And de pine knots burned and blazed, and de Hebrew chillun jest sot round on de coals. "Bring my overcoat, King Nebuchadnezzar," say one of de Hebrew boys. "Hit's a draft in yar and I'm cold, and I don't want to git tuck down wid de phthisic."

"Well, dat whups me," say King Nebuchadnezzar. "I b'lieve I'll go on out and feed my lines. Bring dat boy Daniel out yar so I kin feed him to my lines."

So dey brang Daniel out, but Daniel wa'n't

skeered. He been tawkin' wid de Lawd 'bout dem lines.

"Dem lines ain't hongry," say Daniel.

"Well, you kin stay among 'em to dey gits hongry," say de king.

"Well," say Daniel, "I wish you'd fix me up a bed and bring me some vittles, 'cause I'm gonter git mighty tired sleepin' on de ground wid nothin' but a line for my pillow to dem scoun-d'els gits hongry enough to eat me."

"Dat's jest you and de lines about dat," say Nebuchadnezzar. "I'm goin' and put on my robes and wash my face and hands and git ready for de big doin's tonight."

So dat night ole King Nebuchadnezzar had a mighty feast. All de big folks and de quality folks in de town came, and hit kept de hand-maidens busy dancin' and singin' and makin' music, and hit kept de handmen busy rollin' out de licker and knockin' out de bungs.

"When I invites y'all to come to a mighty feast," say Nebuchadnezzar, "do y'all have a mighty feast or don't you?"

"Yo' Majesty," say all de people, "we does."

"Well, den, is ev'ybody happy?" say Nebu-chadnezzar.

"Don't we look happy?" say de people.

"Well, jest make yo' own fun," say Nebuchadnezzar. So some er de menfolks got to drinkin' de licker outer de bungholes, and some er de women got to passin' out and fallin' to sleep under de tables, and ev'ybody got to carryin' on scandalous.

"Whar all dem solid-gold cups which I tuck f'm de Hebrew boys?" say ole King Nebuchadnezzar.

"Put away," say de haid waiter.

"Well, bring 'em out so My Majesty kin drink some licker outer dem solid-gold drinkin'-cups," say ole King Nebuchadnezzar. And right dar was whar he made a big mistake, 'cause dem cups wa'n't de Hebrew boys' cups. Dem was de Lawd's cups. So 'bout de time ole King Nebuchadnezzar drunk out of a solid-gold cup, de Lawd stepped right through de wall and wrote somethin' on hit, and den stepped right back again.

"I seen a ha'nt," say King Nebuchadnezzar.

"Hit's de licker," say de gal which is settin' in his lap. "Hit'll make you see mighty nigh anything."

"Naw, hit ain't de licker," say Nebuchad-

[248]

nezzar. "Licker makes me see snakes. You can't fool me 'bout licker. I know when I sees snakes. I tell you I seen a ha'nt."

"Well," say de gal, "le's call him over and give him a drink."

"Ain't no time to git funny wid me now, gal," say Nebuchadnezzar. "I sees some writin' on de wall. Dat's what I sees."

"What do hit say?" say de gal.

"I didn't brought my glasses," say Nebuchadnezzar.

"I'm too drunk to read hit, too," say de gal. "Whyn't you call dat boy Daniel which is sleepin' wid de lines? He ain't drunk."

So dey sont for Daniel out in de lines' den.

"Read hit to me, Daniel," say Nebuchadnezzar, "and I'll give you de best job in my kingdom."

So Daniel look at de writin' and den he look at de king. "Ole King Nebuchadnezzar," he say, "you can't give me no job in yo' kingdom, 'cause f'm what I reads yonder on de wall, you ain't got no kingdom no more."

"Is dat a fack?" say Nebuchadnezzar. "What do hit say?"

"It's de Lawd's own handwritin'," say Daniel.

[249]

"Lawd writin' me a letter, is he?" say Nebuchadnezzar. "What he writin' to me, Daniel?"

" 'Dear King Nebuchadnezzar', hit say," say Daniel, " 'Heavy, heavy hangs over yo' haid. Yours truly, Lawd.' "

"Sounds like he's writin' me a riddle instid of a letter," say de king.

"Well, riddle or letter," say Daniel, "dat's what hit say. And hit means dat de Lawd is done got tired er yo' foolishness and is done quit playin' wid you. Hit means dat befo' sunup you ain't gonter be no king no more. Dat is what hit means."

"So de Lawd don't like my style er bein' king?" say Nebuchadnezzar. "Well, I be doggone!"

"De Lawd don't like yo' style and he ain't gonter try to change hit," say Daniel.

"What he gonter do?" say Nebuchadnezzar.

"He gonter change kings," say Daniel.

"Well," say Nebuchadnezzar, "bein' king ain't much fun, anyway. Y'all boys and gals go right on wid de party as long as de licker holds out. I b'lieve I'm gonter go out and eat me a little grass."

A *Preliminary Motion in Judge Pilate's Court*

WELL, hit was a jedge name ole Jedge Pilate and he was a mean jedge. So one day he was settin' back on de bench waitin' for somebody to git into some devilment so he could jedge 'em, so 'bout dat time de door opened and in wawked a gal name Miss Salome.

Miss Salome was a good gal, but she was a dancin' gal. Dancin' was her besettin' sin. So one day she met up wid a preacher name John de Baptist and him and her had some tawk and she promise' to quit dancin'. So de fust thing she knowed yar come de po-lice and arrested John de Baptist charged with Act 1436, Section 4. Dangerous and Suspicious. And quick as Miss Salome yared de news she hauled off and went to see Jedge Pilate.

"You got a mighty good man in jail today, ole Jedge Pilate, Yo' Honor," she say.

"What he been doin'?" say ole Jedge Pilate.

"Nothin'," say Miss Salome.

"I'm gonter 1436 him to death," say ole Jedge Pilate. "I'm gittin' sick and tired of all dese lazy scound'els layin' round town doin' nothin'. Whyn't he git him a job and git to work?"

"He don't has to work, Yo' Honor," say Salome; "he's a preacher."

"Preacher, is he?" say ole Jedge Pilate. "Well efn hit's anything I don't like, hit's preachers. We got too many preachers now and ev'y time I gits a whack at one of 'em I jest lays 'em away."

"You don't like preachers?" say de dancin' gal.

"Not a little bit," say de jedge.

"Well, maybe den, ole Jedge Pilate," say Salome, "maybe you'd like to see a little dancin' done by a good-lookin' woman?" And she struts about a little, fast and wicked, right in front of de jedge.

"I don't see nothin' which looks like a good-lookin' woman about you, gal," say de jedge.

Salome don't say nothin', but she struts around a little more and all at once she reaches up and snatches off her dress!

"Look out dar, gal," say de jedge; but Salome jest th'ows her haid back and laughs, 'cause she's got on another dress right under de one she snatched off.

"Well, dat don't look like much to me," say Jedge Pilate, and Salome cuts another step or two and snatches off dat dress.

Jedge Pilate slap his hand over his eyes and looked out betwixt his fingers, and he seed she got on another dress under dat one, too.

"Gal, you sho wears a heap er clothes," say Jedge Pilate; but Salome jest laughs and backs up and cuts de "jay bird" right in front of him and snatches off another dress.

"Gal, you better be careful de way you on-

[253]

dresses round dis cou't-house, 'cause I's a married man and de ole lady comes round yar sometime," say de jedge. But Salome ain't sayin' a
word; she jest keeps on cuttin' steps and
snatchin' off dresses to she done tore off six
dresses.

Den Salome quits dancin' sort of sad-like and
starts pickin' up de dresses she done scattered
round de cou't-house. "Dis ain't gittin' me nowheres," she say. "I guess ole ugly me better go
on back to de washtub and start scrubbin' clothes
for de white folks."

"Gal, you ain't gonter quit dancin', is you?"
say ole Jedge Pilate. "You jest got goin' good.
Come on and cut a few more steps and snatch off
some more dresses. You does dat purty. You
looks good sheddin' clothes, and de more you
sheds, de purtier you looks."

So Salome drap de dresses and hang her haid
down like she's ashame', and say, "Aw, Jedge,
you don't like to see me dance."

"Yes I does, sugar," say de jedge. "Gal, you's
a good-lookin' gal and you sho kin twist yo'se'f
round de floor. How come I ain't never seed
you befo'? Whar you been keepin' yo'se'f? Yar
I been settin' in dis cou't goin' on two terms and

you ain't never been brang befo' me? Baby, come on and dance some more for de ole jedge."

"Well, Jedge," say Salome, "I'm gonter tell you plain. You ain't never seed me befo' 'cause I'm a nice gal and don't git arrested. But I got a mighty good friend in dat jail, and I ain't got on but jest dis one last dress. Now efn you wants to see me dance some more you got to turn my man outer jail."

De jedge riz up powerful mad. "What you tryin' to do, gal? Contempt my cou't?" he say.

"Nawsuh, Yo' Honor," say Salome, "I ain't tryin' to do nothin'. I jest said what I said. You kin take hit or you kin pour hit back in de jug."

"Well, hit sounds mighty like you's tryin' to git me contempted," say Jedge Pilate.

"I sees I ain't gittin' nowheres wid dis dancin' stuff," say Salome, "so I jest might as well git my dresses and git on home." And she make like she's pickin' up de dresses she done shed.

"How do I know you ain't got on no more dresses under dat one?" say Jedge Pilate.

"Den efn I got on another dress under dis one," say Salome, "jest don't turn my friend aloose." And she sort of starts steppin' 'bout kinder slow, betwixt de jedge and de sunshine.

[255]

"Keep on goin', sugar," say Jedge Pilate. "Le's see dat dance."

So Salome oozed round de cou't-room about twice, slow and steady, lookin' at de jedge and laughin' like she ain't so happy, and de jedge riz up in his chair, powerful intrusted. Den Salome sa'nters up close to de jedge and starts backin' off wid de slow drag.

"Go on and dance hit, gal," say de jedge. "I got bofe eyes shet, but I kin see dat. Go on, gal."

So Salome stiffened up and stuck out her front laig and dragged up wid de "Ninety-one."

"You kin jab my eyes out now, Lawd," say Jedge Pilate, " 'cause hit ain't no need in me lookin' at nothin' else f'm now on. I done seed ev'y thing worth lookin' at."

So Salome stuck out bofe arms straight and bent way over to de side and started pullin' up wid de "Sally Long."

"I ain't lookin' at you, gal," say Jedge Pilate. "I'm settin' yar lookin' at de ceilin'. I ain't payin' you no mind. Le's see you do dat again."

So Salome straightened up and stood on her toes and started de "Floatin'-water Wiggle" and she reach up and start unbuttonin' dat last dress, wid ole Jedge Pilate settin' dar lookin' square at her.

To about dat time de door swings open and one er Jedge Pilate's little boys busts in and says, "Pappy, mamma say dinner is about ready; she say you better come on and wash yo' face and hands and git ready to eat."

*N*igger Deemus

WELL, time kept passin' by and finally hit got to be so many people on de yearth and so many places scattered round yar and yonder to de Lawd jest natchally didn't have time to git around to 'em all. So he got him twelve disciples and marched 'em about de wilderness, learnin' 'em how to preach, so he could go on and 'tend to his yuther business and let de preachers look after de people.

"Now I'm gonter tell y'all a parable," say de Lawd. "Hit was a rich man name Dives and he tuck all his money and goods and put 'em in de house and locked de house and th'owed de key in de well. So dat night he had a dream and one er my angels come down to him in de dream.

" 'Dives,' say de angel, 'how come you lock all yo' money and goods in de house and th'ow de key in de well?'

" ' 'Cause,' say Dives, 'I'm a rich man, and long as can't nobody git to my money and my goods, not even me, I'm gonter keep on bein' a rich man.'

" 'Thou fool,' say de angel. 'Dis night shalt thou dwell wid me in Paradise.'

"So," say de Lawd, "you see hit don't make no diff'unce how much money and goods you got, you can't take hit to heaven wid you when you die."

"Ain't hit de truf, Lawd?" say ole Peter.

So they march along down by de river and de Lawd stop 'em again and gits ready to preach 'em another parable. But 'bout dat time they yar somebody over behind de levee, singin':

"When I gits to heaven I wanter be like Job;
 Le's have a time, le's have a time!
 I wants to wawk all around in my long white robe,
 Shoutin' wid de angels, in de mawnin'!"

"Dat sho is a purty song, ain't hit?" say de Lawd.

"Ain't hit de truf, Lawd?" say Peter.

So dey listen and de song kept right on singin':

> "Matthew, Mark and Luke and John;
> Le's have a time, le's have a time!
> All dem prophets daid and gone,
> Shoutin' wid de angels, in de mawnin'!"

So de Lawd looked over de levee to see who singin'.

"Well, I be doggone!" say de Lawd. "Dat's ole Nigger Deemus singin' dat song. Settin' right yonder on de bank, singin' and fishin'! Come on over yar, Deemus and jine my band. I needs a good bass singer, anyway. And anybody which kin sing like dat ain't got no business wastin' his time fishin'."

"Lawd," say Nigger Deemus, "efn I quits fishin' I's starve to death. Singin' is lots of fun, but you can't eat fun, Lawd."

"I 'tends to de eatin'," say de Lawd. "When my disciples gits hongry, I jest passes a miracle on a rock and turns hit into vittles. Come on."

"Naw, Lawd," say Deemus. "I knows you kin feed ev'ybody you wants to, and I knows you ain't gonter let no man round you go hongry, white or black. But, Lawd, you knows and I knows I ain't got no business goin' round de wilderness wid you and all dem white folks. I knows my place in dis man's town. 'Live and let live,' I say. So I'm jest gonter fish along and have a good time thinkin' 'bout what I'm gonter do when I gits to heaven and gits in my long white robe and won't nobody know is I white or black."

"Nigger Deemus," say de Lawd, "when I tells a man somethin', kin he believe hit, or can't he?"

"He kin, Lawd, ev'y time," say Nigger Deemus.

"Well," say de Lawd, "verily, verily I say unto you, Nigger Deemus, I ain't got no Jim Crow law 'mongst my disciples."

"Dat's right, Lawd," say Nigger Deemus, "you ain't got no Jim Crow law 'mongst yo' disciples. But ——"

"But which, Nigger Deemus?" say de Lawd.

"But hit ain't no Jim Crow law in de votin' round dis town, too," say Nigger Deemus. "But hit's a primary law and hit's a granddaddy-clause law, and de niggers don't do much votin'."

"Well," say de Lawd, "hit ain't no tricks like dat 'mongst my disciples. All a man got to do is repent, believe, and be baptized, white or black. Dey all looks alike to me. I ain't payin' no 'ten-

tion to de color of a man's hide. I'm payin'
'tention to de color of his heart."

"Ain't hit de truf, Lawd?" say Peter.

"Well, Lawd," say Deemus, "de fish ain't bitin'
much, anyway."

So they marched along and ole Nigger Deemus
kinder sidled along behind de yuthers, jest
watchin' and wawkin' whar de Lawd led him.
So purty soon de sun got high so's a man could
reach out and step on de shadder of his own haid.

"Lawd," say Peter, "don't thou think hit's
about dinner time?"

So de Lawd looked up at de sun, and back to
his shadder. "Disciples, stop!" he say.

So all de disciples stopped.

"Disciples, pick up a rock," say de Lawd.

So dey all picked up a rock and lined up and
marched up past de Lawd. And when a man
come by de Lawd passed a miracle on de rock and
turned hit into fried chicken and ham and cake
and beans and all de yuther kind of vittles.

So ole Nigger Deemus hung back, watchin',
to de rest got done, so he reach down and pick
him up a rock and sa'ntered up to de Lawd wid
hit.

"Nigger Deemus," say de Lawd, "I can't do

nothin' wid dat rock. Hit ain't de right kind
er rock, in de fust place, and in de second place,
you got to tote hit in yo' left hand. Go on back
and git you another rock and bring hit to me in
yo' left hand."

So ole Deemus went on back and got another
rock in his left hand and marched up to de Lawd.

De Lawd looked at de rock and den he looked
at Deemus.

"Deemus," say de Lawd, "when you j'ined my
band, I tole you hit wan't no Jim Crow laws and
no Jim Crow tricks in hit, didn't I?"

"Yes, Lawd," say Deemus.

"Well," say de Lawd, "hit ain't. So I'm jest
gonter show you what I kin do wid dat rock and
what I can't do wid hit. 'Cause efn I up and
tells you I can't do nothin' to hit, you liable to
think I'm tryin' to Jim Crow you. So I'm jest
gonter do de best I kin wid hit."

"Lawd," say Deemus, "dat's all anybody kin
do."

So de Lawd r'ared back and clouded up and
wheeled about and made a pass over de rock, and
de rock turned into a little bitty hard lump er
cold cawn bread.

"Hit's de best I could do," say de Lawd. "You

seed hit wid yo' own eyes. Now go on out yonder and git you a sho-'nuff rock. De bigger de better. And maybe efn you gits one big enough I kin pass enough vittles to stay you over to supper time."

So Deemus went on out and got him a big rock. Deemus was a stout man and he got de biggest rock he could see, and he strained hit up to his shoulder and come staggerin' up to de Lawd wid hit.

"Nigger Deemus," say de Lawd, "dat sho is a fine-lookin' rock. Whar'd you git hit?"

"Over yonder," say Deemus.

"Dat's a mighty fine-lookin' rock," say de Lawd. "I bet dat is de ve'y rock I been lookin' for all dis time. Whar'd you say you found hit?"

"Over yonder, Lawd," say Nigger Deemus.

"I knowed hit quick as I laid eyes on hit," say de Lawd. "Dat's de ve'y rock I been huntin' for all dis time. Nigger Deemus, set dat rock down right yar and now and build me a church on hit."